MAN *and*
SPACE
THE NEXT DECADE

BOOKS BY RALPH E. LAPP

Man and Space: The Next Decade
Roads to Discovery
The Voyage of the Lucky Dragon
Radiation: What It Is and How It Affects You
   (with Jack Schubert)
Atoms and People
The New Force
Nuclear Radiation Physics (with H. L. Andrews)
Must We Hide?

RALPH E. LAPP

MAN *and* SPACE

THE NEXT DECADE

ILLUSTRATED

HARPER & BROTHERS
Publishers NEW YORK

dedicated to my wife
Jeannette Fernande

CONTENTS

CONTENTS

. . . Our earth is but a small star in the great universe. Yet of it we can make, if we choose, a planet unvexed by war, untroubled by hunger or fear, undivided by senseless distinctions of race, color or theory. . . .

Prayer written by Stephen Vincent Benét
read by Franklin Delano Roosevelt
United Nations, June 14, 1942

1

THE NEW ENVIRONMENT

IN THIS DECADE man enters the new domain of space. It is quite a new environment for him, so before we plunge into the subject matter we might pause to reconsider both man and space.

Charles Darwin called man "the wonder and the glory of the universe." And Shakespeare gave us a rough definition of space as "this majestical roof fretted with golden fire."

These are elegant words for man and space. But, as we shall see, the new prospects for intelligent life in our universe and the thinning mists of space compel us to re-examine where we fit into the scheme of things. Darwin's revolutionary concept of man's evolution on earth is now a century old; his heresy is accepted. I would add "almost universally," but the word "universe" will be used here in a scientific sense. New scientific

1

data gives us the most tantalizing glimpse of man's origin on earth and, oddly enough, these data may be best extended by going out into space and clutching a bit of debris from a crevasse on the moon or from the surface of Mars.

Shakespeare's "majestical roof" is being sought by modern rockets adorned with inquiring instruments. Man is no longer content to dream or to theorize about the nature of the extra-terrestrial world. The German development of the V-2 rocket and the subsequent ICBM race led to the perfection of huge missiles capable of hurling objects into space.

The United States has launched upon a space program which will, in my opinion, cost a minimum of $18 billion during the 1960-to-1970 period and may, in fact, total twice that amount. The great bulk of the expense goes into developing and constructing massive space vehicles and their powerful engines. It would be wonderful if this great effort were a monument to man's longing to explore the unknown and to seek ultimate truths. But in point of fact the great U.S. effort in this space decade is being made because the Soviets have challenged us. We are engaged in a space race with the Russians. We are in effect "seeking status in space."

Scientists happen to be the beneficiaries of this technological competition and they are also participants in the contest. Scientific findings emanating from space research are hailed—sometimes immodestly—as signaling that the United States "is ahead" or "is forging ahead" in space accomplishments. There surely is a competition between scientists of various nations but it is a gentlemanly and a friendly one. And it is not one overlaid with such urgency that the national treasury need be sacked.

The real reason why the United States is dipping so deeply into its coffers to support space research is that space spectaculars have become symbolic of technological supremacy. Sending a man into a quick orbit around the earth has little scientific value and less urgency, but the United States committed over a third of a billion dollars to this chore. Such is the price tag of space status.

Whatever the reasons why men seek to escape into space, one thing is abundantly clear. The arrow of man's effort points outward from his ancestral home. However mundane the motivation, however partisan the undertaking, the journey into the unknown of space has begun. For the first time in the known history of the planet earth, men have set their sights far beyond their touch. There is to my mind a certain nobility to this enterprise which surmounts the pettiness of the space contest. There is clearly implicit in this soaring venture something that illuminates the inner nature of man.

Man ventures into space because it is the last frontier to be crossed. The planet has been fairly well explored. Space beckons as an inviting arena in which pioneers can make new discoveries and explore the unknown. We happen to be poised to lunge into space because of the technological clash between two competing societies; this has accelerated the dawn of the space age just as the urgent military demand for an A-bomb took us over the threshold of the atomic age faster than would have otherwise been the case. Thus we are probably a full decade and perhaps two decades ahead of the "normal" timetable of the 20th century.

The first space decade promises to be an exciting one for the scientist and for the layman as well. Manned space missions during this period will be limited to modest and quite temporary invasions of the space domain. Many billions of dollars will be spent on developing the vehicles with which to allow astronauts to survive in the space environment. The United States has disclosed a ten-year program of space activities which is ambitious from a purely scientific viewpoint but which appears to some observers, including the writer, to be falling short of the mark if space leadership is to be wrested from the hands of the Soviets.

The U.S. ten-year program does not contemplate landing a man on the moon before 1970. I shall be very surprised if the year 1970 rolls around and a Soviet astronaut has not set foot upon the moon. The world will undoubtedly regard this as a supreme feat of technology—not of a neutral but rather that of a Soviet technology. A Soviet victory in space, especially a triumph of such evident magnitude, will severely erode the prestige of the United States. Lyndon B. Johnson, as chairman of the Senate Committee on Aeronautics and Space Sciences, warned as early as December 18, 1959: "We cannot concede outer space to communism and hold leadership on earth."

Space exploits in 1968 or 1975 will be based upon research carried out over a period of many years. And if this book has a lesson to preach, it is that the U.S. space effort cannot be allowed to be second best. However, I do not intend to indulge in exhortation or dire prophecy. I do wish to make it quite clear that I regard the U.S. space program, as defined in 1960, as rather conservative and inadequately financed. I also hold the view—to add one more editorial touch—that it would be a very fine thing if all the nations of the world could unite in a common effort of space investigation.

With this preface to man's entry into space we turn to man himself. The earth creature we call Homo sapiens, the most highly developed of the primates, is far from an ideal candidate for space travel. He has lived for too long in the same environment and has grown used to it. Although up to the advent of the space age few thought much about the fact, we are all conformists. As human beings we conform to the dictates of our planet. One of the most profound, yet subtle, influencers of our body structures is the earth's gravity. Our skeletal frames, our musculature and some vital organs are closely adapted to the downward pull, or g-force, of the earth. Until the development of modern machines capable of swift acceleration, human beings knew only the one-g pull of the earth. We are, so to speak, one-g people.

Suppose that the earth's gravity was ten times its present value. Had people evolved in their present form, they would weigh almost a ton. Obviously, this much-greater crush of gravity would have produced quite a different breed of man. Physically, the ten-g man would probably have been broad-footed, small but powerfully built and endowed with a strong heart.

This elephantine supposition may serve to make one reflect upon the present form of man. As an energy-dependent machine, man must consume about seven pounds of food and drink each day. The uptake, transport and conversion of this chemical energy runs the essential machinery of the human body. There is no magical process, no fantastic food pill, that lessens this ancient demand. We exclude for this decade any thought of human hibernation aboard spaceships. About the best that one can hope for is that spacemen will be able to trim down the requirement for one ton of food and drink per year by recycling human wastes—or, to put it more bluntly, by rendering urine potable.

Besides edible solids and potable liquids, human beings have a constant demand for oxygen, and more generally, for a life-support system which provides oxygen and other gases in a definite balance. For example, in one day the average man breathes in enough air to fill an 800-gallon tank. This is, of course, a gas of which a fifth is all-important, life-sustaining oxygen. Packaged in liquid form, the daily oxygen requirement weighs about two pounds. A year's supply, including pressure tanks and regulating equipment, might weigh almost a ton.

Man, the air-breather and food-eater, has some obvious limitations as a space traveler. To survive in space for any length of time, he must seal himself up in a weighty capsule within which his earthly environment is duplicated as far as possible. Naturally, the space cabin must be kept at a reasonable temperature; this is not too difficult an assignment for space engineers.

There are other more subtle hazards in space. The weightless condition of the spaceman represents a significant change in man's environment. Astronauts may be exposed to greater radiation hazards such as the great bursts of penetrating rays emitted periodically by our sun. It may even be necessary to provide heavy shields to protect spacemen against the biological effects of space radiation.

The point of these observations is this: manned space flight requires that the spacecraft be massive. For space cruisers of any length the life-support system alone will amount to several tons per astronaut. This is, however, only part of the story. Suppose we wish to send a crew on a relatively short mission—say, to the moon. Naturally, we (not to mention the crew) are interested in round-trip missions. Our moonbound spacecraft must first "escape" from earth, reach the vicinity of the moon and then reduce its speed for a "soft" landing. Escaping from the pull of the earth requires the blast-off of mighty "booster" rockets. Resisting the pull of the moon's gravity requires the backward blast of powerful rocket engines so that the spaceship settles to the lunar surface without a fearful crash. So much for the one-way mission. In order to bring the spaceman back to earth, their capsule must be blasted off from the moon and guided toward the earth. Again powerful rockets are required. All in all, the original spaceship must be of skyscraper proportions.

The very massiveness of manned spacecraft and the hugeness of the rocket engines puts the application of these monstrous devices into the latter part of this decade or even in the 1970's. That is—according to the U.S. timetable for space exploration. The Soviet timetable is not available (I journeyed to the Soviet embassy to inquire about Soviet space plans to check on this point) but the record of Soviet space "firsts" is impressive. The Soviets have the advantage of possessing superior thrust and they thus have the ability to project heavy payloads into space.

I do not mean to imply that manned space flights will not occur in this decade. I distinguish between manned orbital forays and lunar expeditions. The latter come within the framework of true space flight, whereas the former constitute preliminary spatial gymnastics. I realize that some may interpret this remark as a debunking operation, but this is only because there has been so much fantasy published about space. The other day I found my two-year-old son reading a travel book (upside down!); an ardent publisher had brought the space age practically right into the cradle.

Buck Rogers' exploits in the cartoon strips have conditioned many people to believe that space travel is merely a matter of time. I suspect that quite a few citizens could be conned into buying excursion trips to the moon. Although the moon is our nearest neighbor, it is separated by a formidable gap. In this connection I can relate that a prominent U.S. senator in the course of a 1960 Senate inquiry asked a witness if the B-70 airplane "could fly to the moon." Of course, winged flight ceases at an altitude of about 25 miles. Above this point in the atmosphere there is not enough air either to support an air-breathing engine or to sustain aerodynamic flight.

There is no sharp line of demarcation between the earth's atmosphere and space. As a rule of thumb one might say that space begins where winged flight ceases. This definition will not satisfy international lawyers arguing the fine points of national sovereignty. But just as there has been prolonged debate over the three-mile limit and freedom of the high seas, there will be endless controversy on the air-space border. The U-2 incident made the question one of more than academic interest.

In the range of 100 to roughly 500 miles above sea level we deal with what may be called near-earth or low-orbital space. This is the cruising ground for the majority of the satellites, especially those designed to be of some practical value to earth dwellers. Such earth-circling devices take an hour and a half or longer to make one circuit around the globe. At an altitude of about 22,000 miles (somehow or other the term "altitude" sounds odd, so we shall refer to "distance" hereafter), a satellite keeps in step with the earth's rotation; we call this a 24-hour orbit. At a distance of 60 earth radii, or a quarter of a million miles, we find the moon—the earth's only natural satellite.

Although the moon is an object of great interest, many rocket experts look upon it as a way station into space. They feel that a lunar base has many advantages for the deeper penetration of space. Some military spokesmen have even championed a lunar base as having military value—no doubt out of traditional esteem for "high ground."

Our brother planet Mars and our sister neighbor Venus bracket the earth's orbit around our sun. Distances to these fellow-travelers in the solar system depend upon the relative positions of the planets and this is constantly changing as the bodies orbit the sun at different speeds. The actual straight-line separation of earth and Mars may at times be only 35 million miles, but arrow flight in space is impractical. Interplanetary trajectories follow elliptical paths, so that an earth-Mars round-trip course might cover well over one half billion miles.

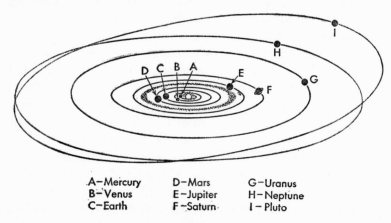

A—Mercury	D—Mars	G—Uranus
B—Venus	E—Jupiter	H—Neptune
C—Earth	F—Saturn	I—Pluto

Fig. 1. The solar system.

The rest of the planets, with the exception of close-in Mercury, describe majestic ellipses at great distances from the sun. The diagram (Fig. 1) shows the relative positions of the so-called giant planets. Jupiter, the colossus of the solar system, is 1,300 times the size of our planet. Beyond it lies Saturn, the planet famous for its rings. Two lesser giants, Uranus and Neptune, complete the main cast of characters for our stellar system. We must include in a minor role planet Number 9, Pluto, which is roughly the size and mass of the earth. Pluto wanders to a maximum of almost 4½ billion miles from the sun and takes almost 248 years (earth years) to complete an orbit.

The outer recesses of our whirling family of planets hold less interest than the inner zone, which is populated by closer relatives. This is fortunate since the kinds of space vehicles which appear to be practical in the next decade or two limit us to the inner family of planets. And in this decade of the sixties our explorations of other planets will have to be by proxy. Vehicles that are practical to construct soon can project moderate payloads at interplanetary range. These payloads will be crammed with ingenious instruments which make a number of physical measurements and relay the information back to earth.

Long before man sets foot on the moon, instrument packages will have preceded him. Some of the gadgets currently under development are known as telerobots. They are intricate mobile devices which trundle out from a lunar spaceship to survey the immediate moonscape. All of which is, of course, getting far ahead of our story. We have first to leave the earth before we can venture into space and seek out the mysteries now hidden on the moon and elsewhere. And to leave this bountiful planet, all outward bound spacecraft must escape from the age-old, but no longer irresistible, attraction of the earth's gravity. We begin our entry into space by examining the problem of escape. If, perchance, this introduction to space mechanics should seem a bit stiff and overly technical, I can only offer the encouragement that the rest of the book is less formidable and quite a lot more exciting.

This next decade is going to be most stimulating and I suggest that those who tackle the space problem as intelligent laymen will find the progress of space developments a fascinating and enjoyable feature of the modern world. To my mind, we are entering a period of intense intellectual activity. We are turning the first pages in a many-chaptered book of life and the universe.

2

THE ETERNAL FORCE

MAN'S most ancient and most constant companion on earth is gravity. It is the central force which directs our lives, determines the annual pilgrimage of the planets and structures the architecture of the universe. The invisible fingers of this eternal force reaches out over limitless stretches of space. All objects in space, whether stars, galaxies or a minuscule rocket, must obey the laws of gravity. Nothing is exempt, neither a rock thrown into the air nor an exploding star.

An object falls to earth because of the attraction between it and the earth—we call this "gravitational attraction." Galileo is reputed to have confounded his colleagues by leaning out from the Tower of Pisa and dropping spheres of wood and metal. Almost everyone believed that heavy objects fall faster than light ones, but then they never took the trouble to use the experimental approach of Galileo. He measured the effect by noting which sphere hit the ground first, and to the chagrin of

10

his colleagues he discovered that both the light wood ball and the heavy metal sphere hit the earth at the same time. Naturally, a piece of paper or a feather slips to the ground more slowly than a chunk of metal, but this is because of air resistance. In the absence of air both the feather and the piece of metal descend at the same rate.

When we study the course of a falling object, we learn about the laws of motion which are so fundamental to understanding man's entry into space. For only by comprehending the laws of motion can we explain the orderly orbits of the planets and the seemingly more erratic behavior of comets and meteors.

Throughout the ages men have looked up at the heavens and gazed in awe at the glittering majesty of far-off fires. Even the earliest observers, earth-burrowing cavemen, must have scanned the skies, and perhaps a late-roving hunter guided his feet back to his home with the help of friendly stars. Many a shepherd, watching his flock by night, must have sensed the time pattern of the stars cartwheeling above. Polynesian natives ventured across thousands of miles of the Pacific without benefit of compass. How much they knew about the techniques of celestial navigation is not known, but they must have been shrewd observers of the night sky, canny enough to use the stars as guide lights.

Those who first plotted the course of the planets had to devise exceedingly complex models in order to "explain" their paths in the sky. This, of course, came about because man put himself squarely in the center of things and sought an egocentric explanation of the motion of heavenly bodies. It was unthinkable that the earth should not be the hub from which all else radiated. In addition to the fixed notion that the earth was the center of all things, there persisted up through the centuries the twin ideas that the universe was finite in dimension and that it was ruled by laws unlike those which applied to our earth.

Copernicus made his great contribution by substituting the sun for the earth as the center of things. While Copernicus still regarded our solar system as the hub of the universe, his advocacy of a sun-centered rather than an earth-centered system was revolutionary enough for his times. Galileo strongly supported the Copernican view and did much to win its acceptance. Man was now on the right track and the earth was assigned its proper place in the scheme of things.

Galileo constructed a 30-power telescope in the first decade of the 17th century and suddenly a vast new world came into view. The naked eye can view but a few thousand stars and can see no detail except on the moon. In 1609 Galileo was the first to perceive that Jupiter has four moons. He demonstrated the power of the new instrument which was to make astronomy into a precise science. But even without the power of optical telescopes, Tycho Brahe, the Danish astronomer, took elaborate and painstaking measurements of the motions of the heavenly bodies. These new data were placed in the hands of the brilliant if mystical thinker, Johannes Kepler. Early in the 17th century he formulated three basic laws governing the motion of planets. A vast amount of astronomical data on planetary motion was suddenly compressed into the framework of these simple equations.

Kepler's first law states that all the planets move about the sun, following an elliptical path. The sun stands at one focus, or key point, of this ellipse. The second law has to do with the speed in orbit of a planet; when the planet draws closest to the sun (perihelion) it travels at its highest speed, while when farthest away (aphelion) the planet moves at its slowest speed. Kepler expressed this relation in a quantitative manner which need not concern us here. The third law of motion which the German scientist formulated relates the time required for one orbital circuit of a planet to its mean distance from the sun.

Tycho Brahe's labor of many years—his great store of observational data—fitted neatly into Kepler's equations. Much was accomplished but Kepler's laws were keyed to observational data; they were not birthed in theory. There strode upon the scene a young Englishman whose intellect was like a powerful searchlight illuminating great areas of ignorance. His name was

Isaac Newton. He pondered a wide variety of physical problems —the nature of light, the motions of the planets and the riddle of the moon.

The story is told, and it is probably true, that one day young Newton was relaxing in his garden, beneath an apple tree. An apple fell to earth (there is no proof that it struck Newton on the head) and the young philosopher asked himself a profound question: Why did it fall? More than that, he asked: "Why does not the moon fall like the apple?" Newton knew, of course, that the moon revolves about the earth once every 27.3 days. He knew that the circular path of the moon in its earth orbit and that of the planets around the sun must be due to some attractive force. Another way of putting it is to say that for circular motion to occur there must be some central force, otherwise the moon would fly away from the earth and the planets would zoom away from the sun.

Newton wondered whether the central force attracting the moon to the earth might be the same as that pulling the apple to earth. The moon orbits the earth at a distance of one quarter million miles and we can compute that it has an average speed in orbit of about 2,300 miles per hour. Anyone who has watched a wet wheel or bicycle tire spinning rapidly knows that drops fly off in a straight line at a tangent to the rim. Were there no contrary force acting on the moon it would fly off into space. Obviously, some force of attraction keeps the moon in orbit.

Newton assumed that this force acting on the moon was the same as that which pulls an apple to the ground. At the earth's surface we say that this force of gravity has a value of one g. What, then, is the value of the earth's gravity at a distance out in space—say, at the moon's orbit? Using a sophisticated mathematical approach (Newton actually invented a new branch of mathematics—the calculus—for his analysis) the great British scientist propounded his Universal Law of Gravitation: "Every material particle in the universe exerts a force of attraction on every other particle equal to the product of their masses and inversely proportional to the square of their intervening distance."

This famous law of Newton can be illustrated as follows. If we take one g as the value of gravity at the earth's surface, i.e., at one earth radius, then if we go out into space in an orbit 4,000 miles above sea level the value of gravity at this point should be one fourth that at sea level. We double our distance from the earth's center and the value of gravity decreases by the inverse square of two, i.e., one fourth. At six earth radii (i.e., 20,000 miles above sea level) the value of gravity drops to one thirty-sixth of one g. And at the moon's separation of 60 earth radii, the force drops to 1/3,600 g. This rapid drop-off in the earth's pull on any object means that the gravity barrier, i.e., the hill that must be surmounted, is greatest at or near the earth's surface. As a rocket proceeds out into space it is acted upon by weaker and weaker gravitational forces.

Newton's universal law proved to be a great unifying concept which allowed purely empirical relations to be understood. In fact, Kepler's three laws flowed directly from a simple application of Newton's law. Kepler's laws were even shown to need modification and Newton derived five significant additions, but these do not concern us in our elementary treatment of gravity and planets.

The great genius of Newton is revealed in his monumental work *The Mathematical Principles of Natural Philosophy*. In it, Newton laid the groundwork for the science of mechanics—the basis of all engineering and to a great extent that of celestial mechanics. Whether we are concerned with bridge construction or the trajectory of a comet or the path of a satellite, Newton's *Principia* published in 1687 is the bible to use.

Newton's three fundamental laws of motion are the foundation stones upon which to build our knowledge of both earth science and space science.

The first law refers to uniform motion. It states that a body moving uniformly in a straight line continues on its course, undisturbed and indefinitely, unless acted upon by some external force. A special case of uniform motion is that of a body at rest, i.e., zero motion, in which case it remains at rest throughout eternity unless acted upon by some force. To illustrate Newton's first law, let us consider a rocket traveling at constant velocity in free space. It will continue on its straight-line course forever. Naturally, there is really no such thing as "free space" because the forces of gravity (from the sun and stars) reach out to infinity. Sooner or later, a rocket would feel the pull of some celestial body and would be swerved from its course.

As a matter of practical concern, a rocket fired from earth has to escape from the earth's gravitational field. We have seen how the earth's gravitational force drops off so that at the moon's orbit it is 3,600 times less than at sea level. A rocket zooming away from the earth feels less of the gravity tug from its place of origin but it soon comes under the powerful influence of the sun's gravitational attraction.

The second law of motion deals with acceleration. We define acceleration as a change of speed or velocity. We say that a motorcar accelerates quickly when we change its velocity from zero to 60 miles per hour in less than a minute. A light motorcycle accelerates faster than a big truck. Of two cars of exactly the same weight, the one with the more powerful engine can accelerate more quickly. Newton's second law simply relates acceleration (a) to the force (f) acting on a body of mass (m). This is the famous $f = m \times a$ law. It says that when a force (f) acts upon a mass (m) it will produce an acceleration (a) given by the $f = m \times a$ relation. Furthermore, the motion takes place in the direction along which the force acts.

Suppose that we apply Newton's second law to the force of gravity. This force pulls any object of mass (m) toward the earth's center and if the object is free to fall (as down an elevator shaft) it keeps accelerating downward. The acceleration due to gravity has a value of one g at the earth's surface. The weight (w) of an object of mass (m) is given by the $f = m \times a$ relation, as $w = m \times g$. People tend to confuse mass and weight; the thing to remember is that weight is merely a convenient, local (meaning "here on earth") measure of a body's mass. Mass is a fundamental quantity to the physicist because it does not depend upon gravity as does weight. A man of mass (m) may weigh 180 pounds at the earth's surface but on the moon he would weigh only 30 pounds. The acceleration due to the moon's gravity is only one sixth as much as on earth; this is because the moon has only $\frac{1}{81}$ as much mass as the earth and only about half its diameter. Once man sets foot on the moon, he will be a real lightweight and will be able to bounce around with the greatest of ease. Whereas the present high-jumping record on earth is over 7 feet, on the moon this would be child's play.

Newton's second law is important when applied to rocket propulsion. Suppose that we have a rocket which weighs ten tons, fuel included, and we wish to have this vehicle attain high speed. Vertical take-off requires that the applied thrust exceed the vehicle weight by about one-third. Thus in this case the thrust required would be about 27,000 pounds. This thrust is generated by the rocket engine operating at constant power. The final or burn-out velocity attained by the rocket depends mainly upon the total thrust generated by the rocket engine. This, in turn, depends upon the amount of fuel burned and the energy released per pound of fuel. An obvious way to boost the speed is to find a fuel that is more energy-rich; we shall have more to say about rocket fuels shortly. Another way to propel the rocket to higher final speed (known as burn-out velocity) is to split the rocket into two stages. Each stage is equipped with its own engine and fuel tanks and when the first stage burns out, it is simply discarded. This procedure eliminates the dead weight of the first-stage engine and structure, so that a smaller amount of mass is left to be propelled by the second-stage engine. Even though the second-stage engine may be much smaller and provide less thrust, the mass being accelerated is correspondingly less and by this stratagem the final velocity of the second stage can be made two or even more times that of the first stage.

In order to "lift off," a rocket must have an acceleration

greater than that due to gravity. Powerful rockets are often propelled upward with a force of ten g's or more. This is, of course, momentary and a spaceman riding inside a capsule would be subjected to this crushing acceleration for only a matter of minutes, but during this time he would "weigh" ten times as much as normal. A 180-pound astronaut would weigh 1,800 pounds.

Once a rocket designed to place a man in orbit attains its desired velocity and the engines are shut down, the vehicle will glide around the world at constant velocity. For low orbits, i.e., several hundred miles above sea level, an orbiting vehicle must travel with a speed of five miles per second or 18,000 miles per hour. A man riding in such a vehicle will be weightless. Like the moon, he will be constantly falling toward the earth and, like a man falling freely in space, he will have zero weight. Should one wish to provide the astronaut with a sense of weightiness, his space capsule could be spun on its axis. Thus any degree of "artificial gravity" could be created for the occupant of the whirling space device.

Newton's third law of motion may be summed up as "action and reaction." When one body exerts a force on another, then that body must necessarily exert an equal and opposite force upon the other. In effect, this third law says that forces always occur in pairs and that for every action there must be a reaction. A prominent manufacturer of rocket engines has the firm name Reaction Motors. The rocket principle is in fact one that was employed in the 13th century by the Chinese, who were the first to develop explosive powder. They fashioned very crude rockets out of tubes which were packed with a mixture of fast-burning powder. When this powder was ignited, a stream of hot gas spewed out of the tube and the primitive rocket whooshed into the air. Rockets might have enjoyed greater popularity as instruments of destruction in early days had they been more accurate. They lacked proper guidance and could not be relied upon to hit a target.

The gun became a weapon of choice because it could be

aimed with greater accuracy than a rocket. In principle a gun is simply a barrel, open at one end, in which one places a propellant charge and a solid bullet or, alternatively, a shell which combines the solid projectile and explosive powder in a single cartridge. When the propellant is detonated the solid grains of gunpowder explode and produce a rapidly expanding gas. The latter propels the bullet down the barrel and expels it with high velocity. At the same time there is an equal and opposite reaction, or "kick," of the gun as it recoils against the shoulder of the gunner. In the case of artillery pieces, the whole gun assembly recoils and provision is made to take up this impact; in some cases the artillery piece is allowed to roll backward on tracks.

Imagine that we could suspend a gunner in space and provide him with a plentiful supply of ammunition. Every time he fires his gun he will recoil in the opposite direction. Since he is not anchored to *terra firma* where he could absorb the recoil, our space gunner will be accelerated backward. The faster he fires his gun, the greater will be his acceleration. If instead of a hail of bullets expelled from his gun, he allowed the propellant to burn continuously and produce a jet of hot gas, he would then have a true rocket engine. A modern jet aircraft sucks in air for burning its fuel; if it could carry its own oxygen supply it would become a winged rocket.

A common misconception about rocket propulsion is that it involves a pushing against something—either the earth or the atmosphere. Actually, when the rocket thunders into the high altitudes where there is almost a vacuum (and nothing to push against), its engines work even better than at sea level. The push or thrust of the gas expanding in the combustion chamber is exerted against the upper part of this chamber. It is this thrust that drives the rocket upward.

If the stream of exhaust gas expelled from a burning rocket engine is well controlled, the rocket will rise slowly from its launch pad and "lift off." The rocket literally hangs in a state of precarious balance at this critical point. Any serious instability in the propellant stream could cause the rocket to deviate from its vertical climb. To appreciate this fact, one has only to consider the random path of a balloon which is allowed to move freely with its filling end open to the air. Any child knows that the balloon cavorts in the air as the gas propels it first in one direction and then in another. In a high-thrust rocket engine the propellant stream must be carefully controlled to provide constant thrust. Since most of the vehicles we will consider use liquid fuels, it is imperative that the combustion of the fuel with its oxidizer (usually liquid oxygen) be uniform.

A modern military rocket such as the Atlas or Titan is a marvel of plumbing. Since the main requirement of smooth propulsion is uniform combustion, powerful pumps must be carefully regulated to supply the right mixture of jet fuel and liquid oxygen to the combustion chamber. The great bulk of any liquid-fuel rocket consists of massive fuel tanks. In the case of the Titan the main tanks are housed in the 55-foot-high first stage which is eight feet in diameter. The whole structure resembles a huge rifle cartridge almost 100 feet long.

When the Titan is launched, over 100 gallons of fuel mixture are pumped into the combustion chamber every second. A small cupful of gasoline makes an impressive bang so it is no wonder that the burning of jet fuel with liquid oxygen should create such a roaring inferno of flame as one observes at the launch pad. The total thrust of the Titan's first stage represents a force of 300,000 pounds. Starting from rest, the Titan rises slowly off its pad and seems to hover in the air. Then it rushes headlong on its vertical path and disappears from view. It streaks upward at a rate exceeding 5,000 miles per hour, and after two minutes burn-out of the first stage occurs. To carry along the dead weight of the empty fuel tanks, pumps, combustion chamber and structure would be prohibitive. So this useless hulk is detached from the second stage by means of small explosive charges.

Now the 80,000-pound-thrust engine of the second stage is ignited and the rocket again accelerates swiftly. There is less mass to propel so the second stage soars upward. In addition, the rocket is now far beyond the palpable atmosphere and there is negligible air resistance. Driven upward in an arcing trajectory by the gushing blue flame of the rocket, the second stage attains its final and critical velocity of 15,000 miles per hour. The final speed is precisely determined within close limits and the "attitude" of the rocket at burn-out is adjusted so that the missile is aimed in the right direction. From this point on, as the missile hurtles upward on its lofty arc, it proceeds like a stone thrown into the air. It is on a ballistic trajectory and no further alterations are made in its course.

We can think of the ballistic missile as being aimed like an artillery piece. But instead of a short barrel pointed in the right direction, the ICBM is directed along an air corridor and is kept on course by sensing equipment contained within the rocket itself. The main engine can be steered by virtue of a special mounting and fine adjustments can be made by small side jets. So accurate is the guidance equipment nestled within the Titan that operational missiles can impact their warheads well within a circle three miles in diameter. This means that a weapon of this kind fired at Grand Central Station in New York City from a Soviet missile site would probably miss its target by a distance of not more than the width of Manhattan Island.

The cost of hurling objects against the force of gravity is considerable. For example, the payload of an ICBM of the most modern design is about three tons, or roughly forty times less than the total weight of the missile. All costs included, such a missile represents an investment of over $35 million. This means that the transportation charge for an ICBM warhead is about $6,000 per pound. Such a high cost does not augur well for commercial applications such as intercontinental missile mail. However, once the development costs of a missile are written off and one makes allowance for less expensive designs, payload costs should go down sharply. I can conceive of costs dropping to $200 per pound. On this basis a space-age citizen, posting a half-ounce missile letter, would pay postage of $6.34.

If these costs seem high, we must realize that once we leave the earth and head into space, things become even more expensive. The basic reason for this is that the weight of the payload projectable into space gets smaller and smaller as one strives to penetrate deeper and deeper into space. We can visualize the problem as the scaling of invisible gravity barriers or hills. To take an earthly example, consider a motorist who attempts to climb a hill by gunning his car at the bottom of the incline and thereafter coasting to the top. There is a definite velocity that he must attain to reach the top of a given hill. The higher the hill, the greater must be the velocity at the point where the driver takes his foot off the accelerator (this corresponds to "burn-out velocity" for a rocket). To reach higher velocity, assuming that the driver jams his foot to the floor board, a more powerful engine is required.

Sending rockets into space is also done on a "gun and coast" basis. Thrust is developed during the first hundred or so miles of its flight; thereafter, the rocket is "dead." It streaks along its trajectory due to its initial impulse. In the case of a "sounding rocket," which is one sent straight up from earth, the altitude it reaches is as follows: 170 miles for a velocity of 5,000 miles per hour, 720 miles for double this velocity and almost 7,000 miles for a speed of 20,000 mph. As the sounding rocket climbs higher, it loses velocity until it reaches its zenith and falls back to earth.

To escape into space and leave the earth's environment, a rocket needs to attain a velocity of about 25,000 miles per hour. This is called escape velocity. To project a ballistic missile at intercontinental range requires a missile speed of 15,000 mph. ICBM's were perfected as a matter of military necessity and the rocket engines so developed were to serve as the work horses for the early years of the space era.

3

THE SOVIET
BREAKTHROUGH

SOVIET and U.S. ballistic missiles have a common parentage. They are both offshoots of the V-2 missile program of World War II. Hitler seized upon the "wonder weapon" of German technology and backed the missile program to the tune of 350 million gold marks or roughly $150 million. It is estimated that six years of time and 18,000 man-years of technical activity were required to bring the development to fruition.

The V-2 was an impressive rocket which could be turned out on a mass-production basis. It was not highly accurate, often missing its target by ten or 15 miles at 200-mile range, but it symbolized the birth of the missile age. Nazi drawing boards held plans for A9/A10 rockets—huge, multiple-stage engines of war with which Hitler dreamed of laying siege to North America. In addition to the paper plans, the Germans could lay claim

22

to having perfected a skillfully engineered propulsion unit—a liquid-fuel engine which generated a thrust of 56,000 pounds. The design was so good that it served as a prototype for rocket engines a decade later.

The climactic conclusion of World War II, highlighted by the revelation of the striking power of the A-bomb, was followed by disclosures of many technological innovations—proximity fuses, radar, infrared devices, to name but a few. A rash of speculation broke out about the future technology of war, and the ocean-spanning ballistic missile received public mention as a weapon of war. Dr. Vannevar Bush, wartime head of the U.S. military-technological effort, testified on December 3, 1945, before a U.S. Senate committee:

There has been a great deal said about a 3,000-mile high-angle rocket. In my opinion, such a thing is impossible today and will be impossible for many years. The people who have been writing these things that annoy me, have been talking about a 3,000-mile high-angle rocket, shot from one continent to another, carrying an atomic bomb and so directed as to be a precise weapon which would land exactly on a certain target, such as a city.

I say, technically, I don't think anybody in the world knows how to do such a thing, and I feel confident it will not be done for a very long period of time to come. . . . I think we can leave that out of our thinking. I wish the American public would leave that out of their thinking.

Viewed in the light of subsequent developments, Dr. Bush appears to have been a poor prophet. There was, however, an element of technical justification for his pessimism: The United States had no long range missile program at the time and the A-bomb was a five-ton monstrosity. To be effective, such a bomb would have to land within a mile or two of its target. Such accuracy for an intercontinental missile seemed unattainable. We are not privileged to know the reasoning of Soviet planners on this score, but apparently they picked up the V-2 development where the Germans left off and kept plugging away at a ballistic missile program. At first the Soviets focused their efforts on intermediate-range missiles and later shifted their sights to ICBM's.

German missile success had impressed some leaders in the Pentagon and in April and June of 1946 the Army Air Forces awarded contracts totalling $1,893,000 to industry for research on Project MX-774. This was the code name for the U.S. long-range ballistic-missile program. On July 8, 1947, the Army canceled the contracts abruptly as technical pessimism prevailed over military enthusiasm for a new weapon. The project was not officially revived until January of 1951 when the U.S. Air Force awarded a contract for Project MX-1593, which aimed at the development of an ICBM named the Atlas.

On November 1, 1952, the United States tested its first hydrogen bomb. The device, code-named Mike, was detonated with an explosive power equal to 12 million tons of TNT (i.e., 12 megatons). Although it was not a deliverable bomb—it weighed about 60 tons—bomb expert Dr. John von Neumann believed that the gadget could be shrunk to a few tons in weight. The Hungarian-born mathematical genius had participated in pioneering the first A-bomb and, more than any other government advisor, Dr. von Neumann appreciated the impact which an H-bomb warhead could have on missile war.

While Dr. von Neumann worried about Soviet nuclear progress, a highly secret defense project succeeded in developing new long-range radar with which to peek inside the Soviet borders and detect rocket firings. One of these radar installations was secretly completed on a military base in Turkey. "By 1953, this equipment demonstrated unequivocally . . ." Mr. Roy Johnson, as director of the Defense Department's Advanced Research Projects Agency, disclosed before a Congressional committee, "that the Soviet Union was well along the road to the production of rocket missiles." Mr. Johnson claimed that this single piece of information caused the U.S. government to reverse its previous position on the ICBM. Others with equal authority assert that the covert information was disregarded by policymakers. On balance, it appears that the Defense leaders paid little heed to the radar data on Soviet missiles and that events were more influenced by the thermonuclear breakthrough.

Late in the summer of 1953 the Soviets tested an H-bomb of their own design and proved that their nuclear technology was not lagging. Their success with the hydrogen bomb jolted U.S. officials. Von Neumann was appointed to head up an Air Force advisory group to review the ICBM problem. On February 10, 1954, von Neumann's Strategic Missiles Evaluation Committee recommended that "the ballistic missile program—the ICBM—be accelerated to the maximum extent that technology would permit." This policy was approved by the National Security Council in September of the same year, when it assigned first priority to the development of the ICBM.

The problem was no longer political or military; it was now technical. What would our technology permit? The answer to this question was to have the utmost significance for the U.S. space program. But at the time technical decisions were made on the ICBM, no serious thought was given to nonmilitary missiles, i.e., space vehicles. Our experts decided that the "maximum . . . that technology would permit" was an ICBM which eventually turned out to be the Atlas rocket. In other words, our rocket designers fixed upon an ICBM with a thrust of roughly 360,000 pounds, sufficient to deliver an H-bomb warhead.

Soviet rocket experts had fixed upon an ICBM design long before they tested their first H-bomb. Not having in mind a lighter-weight H-warhead, the Soviet experts had to reckon with an immensely heavy A-bomb. Therefore, they made every effort to develop the most powerful rocket engine that was possible. We know now that they set their sights on a rocket with twice the thrust of our Atlas or Titan.

Once success was attained in their H-bomb project, Soviet rocket experts must have realized that they had overshot the mark in designing an oversize ICBM. To be sure, it could carry an even more potent hydrogen warhead, but it was clear that it had excess thrust capacity. When one has too much of something, it is the essence of wisdom to find new uses for it. Soviet scientists urged that the Soviet Union capitalize on its overpowered rocket by using it to launch satellites into orbit around the earth.

Some of the scientists who had contributed brilliantly to the Russian hydrogen project were enthusiastic about turning their talents to a new field of endeavor. It is known that scientists had their arguments with officials in the Kremlin. Soviet military leaders were not happy about the space program, but the scientists won their point and received a go-ahead on their satellite program. Armed with the oversize ICBM as a launch vehicle, Soviet scientists proceeded to draw up ambitious space plans.

U.S. scientists were not lacking in imagination or in enthusiasm for space exploration. In fact, shortly after the war a group of U.S. scientists submitted to the military establishment a proposal "for the development of an artificial satellite" to circle the earth. They even had the insight to forecast that a successful orbital flight would have "profoundly significant impact" the world over. It goes without saying that the decision on the ICBM precluded any action on the satellite proposal. However, the proposal must have stimulated a few in the Pentagon, because in December, 1948, Defense Secretary Forrestal mentioned an "earth satellite vehicle."

It was somewhat futuristic for scientists to propose satellite programs long before the United States had attained any proficiency in ballistic missiles. But in the year 1952 the Defense Department budgeted over $1 billion to missile programs, or almost as much as had been spent in the previous five years. Most of the effort concentrated on rather short-range, surface-to-surface and air-defense missiles, but the Army made steady progress in developing a large missile. Scientists, sensing the potential space application for the Army ballistic missiles, dreamed of artificial satellites and space flights. Some even dreamed out loud and some broke into print with very ambitious space plans. *Collier's* magazine for March 22, 1952, featured the space issue and a proposal by Dr. Wernher von Braun, technical director of the Army Ordnance Guided Missiles Development Group at Huntsville, Alabama. Amplifying proposals made at the First Annual Symposium on Space Travel (Hayden Planetarium, New York; October, 1951), Dr. von Braun proposed a $4 billion program to build a 7,000-ton satellite-rocket.

At the Third Symposium on Space Travel (May 4, 1954) scientists scaled down their proposals. Dr. S. Fred Singer, professor of physics at the University of Maryland, put forth his "Minimum Orbital Unmanned Satellite of the Earth," or Mouse, proposal. This called for a 100-pound satellite to be launched into a 200-mile-high orbit. Dr. Singer estimated that this feat could be accomplished for somewhat more than $1 million per attempt. At the same time Commander R. C. Truax of the Navy's Guided Missiles Division, Bureau of Aeronautics, pleaded for a citizens' crusade to launch an artificial satellite. Quite evidently, he despaired of finding military support for the venture.

U.S. scientists finally turned to purely civilian agencies to promote a satellite program. This was late in 1954 and early 1955, when a thaw in U.S.-Soviet relations—at least enough of a warm-up to permit Soviet participation in scientific conferences —alerted American scientists to the strong possibility that the Soviets were pushing a vigorous space program. In the United States, the National Academy of Sciences, a rather somnolent organization of elder scientists, teamed up with the National Science Foundation (a highly conservative arm of government) and agreed to support a modest satellite program.

On July 29, 1955, the White House issued an announcement revealing that plans had been approved "for the construction of a small, unmanned, earth-circling satellite vehicle to be used for basic scientific observations." Such was the publicity debut of Project Vanguard. It triggered the release of a vast flood of news stories about the grapefruit-sized satellite which would orbit the planet. The drumfire of publicity, begun in 1955, was sustained throughout 1956 and mounted in tempo in the next year as the launch date for Vanguard I drew near.

The Soviets were not nearly so closemouthed as they are often believed to be; the fact is that some of their publications gave details of their satellite—specifying the communication's radio frequency to be used. Dr. A. D. Nesmeyanov, President of the U.S.S.R. Academy of Sciences, predicted in the June 8, 1957, issue of *Pravda*: "Soon, literally within the next months, our planet will acquire another satellite." No one paid much attention to such revelations. I should qualify this observation because a few experts working for the RAND Corporation, an Air Force contractor, pieced together clues about the Soviet space program. In the summer of 1957 they concluded in a report:

The red letter date on the Soviet astronautical calendar is September 17, 1957. This is the 100th anniversary of the birth of K. E. Tsiolkovski, the founder of the science of astronautics. Though it comes rather early in the current International Geophysical Year, there could be no more fitting way of celebrating this occasion—from the Russian point of view—than to establish the first artificial earth satellite in honor of Konstantin Eduardovich Tsiolkovski.

The prestige and propaganda value to be gained from a premier launching of an earth satellite, whether instrumented or not, undoubtedly present a circumstance too attractive for the opportunists in the Kremlin to ignore.

The prophecy hidden in this secret Air Force study was not borne out on the "red-letter" day of September 17, 1957. Perhaps the Soviets tried and failed, or possibly the countdown was stopped when a defect developed. But on October 4 the world was electrified when Radio Moscow made the dramatic announcement that *Iskustvennyi Sputnik Zemli* (artificial fellow-traveler around the earth) had been successfully placed in orbit.

Sputnik I was shot into orbit from an undisclosed launch site somewhere on Kazakhstan's arid steppes. A glistening sphere not quite two feet in diameter, weighing 184 pounds, it was ejected from the last stage of the oversize ICBM which was adapted for propelling the object to high velocity. Upon being injected into orbit, Sputnik I actuated a mechanism releasing its antenna. Four metal rods, five to ten feet in length, snapped into position and the *beep-beep-beep* voice of the world's first artificial satellite was heard.

The orbital period, that is, the time required for a satellite to complete one circuit around the world, is determined by the radius of its circular orbit. The following table illustrates how the period lengthens for higher and higher orbits:

HEIGHT IN MILES	PERIOD	
100	1 h 27 m	
200	1 h 30 m	Low Earth-orbit
500	1 h 40 m	
1,000	1 h 58 m	Medium Earth-orbit
5,000	4 h 46 m	High Earth-orbit
10,000	9 h 16 m	
22,300	24 h	Earth-period
235,000	27 d 7 h	Moon-period

Sputnik I had a period of 96 minutes, corresponding to a circular radius between 200 and 500 miles, but as we shall see it followed an elliptical path.

The orbit of Sputnik I is drawn to scale in Fig. 2. Because the satellite received a trifle too much push, it did not assume

Fig. 2. Orbit of the first satellite is shown in relation to the earth, approximately to scale. (The sequence of drawings on these pages is adapted from *Scientific American,* Vol. 197, No. 6 [1957].)

THE SOVIET BREAKTHROUGH

a perfectly circular orbit, but when drawn to scale the elliptical path appears to be almost a perfect circle. As viewed by a Russian observer, Sputnik I was sent on a northeast course which intersected the equator at an angle of 65 degrees (see Fig. 3). Since the pull of the earth's gravity is directed to the center of our globe, a satellite is constrained to move in an orbit whose plane passes through the center of the earth. By the time the satellite made one complete trip around the globe in

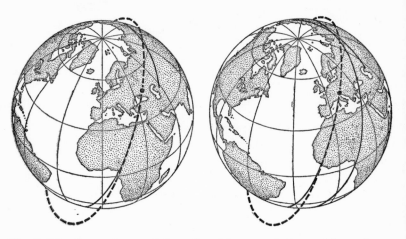

Fig. 3. The first and second Sputnik orbits around the world are shown with their shadow paths projected on the earth's surface.

96 minutes, the earth naturally rotated on its axis from west to east. Thus instead of appearing directly over its launch site after one orbit, the device streaked through the skies at a point much farther to the west. This westward shift is shown diagrammatically in Fig. 3, where it will be noted that the orbit crossed the vicinity of the Black Sea. The orbiting can be visualized as analogous to winding a piece of twine around a ball. Fig. 4 illustrates the composite of all the orbits described in a single day. Lines marked by arrows represent shadow paths of Sputnik on the earth's surface. Total mileage logged in one day's travel amounted to 400,000 miles.

To many on earth, the untiring glide of Sputnik I around the globe must have appeared as perpetual motion. But as the weeks passed the Russian speedster showed signs of tiring. On January 4, 1958, Sputnik's fate was sealed; it plunged into the lower atmosphere and ended its spectacular career in a mass of flame. It was a small thing, a very small thing indeed, which brought the satellite back to earth. Consider, first of all, the original orbit of the world's first satellite. It veered from a

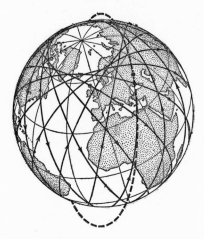

Fig. 4. The shadow paths of Sputnik I are shown for a full day's orbiting around the earth.

perigee, or closest approach to earth, of 142 miles to an apogee of 588 miles. At the latter distance there is so little air that if the satellite spun around the earth at this altitude, never dipping lower, it would have stayed aloft for over a century. But each time it approached perigee, the satellite raced through a less nearly perfect vacuum. The space 142 miles above sea level contains a slight amount of air—not much, to be sure, but even wisps of atmosphere can offer resistance to an object moving with a speed of almost 18,000 miles per hour. This atmospheric resistance produces a drag on a fast-moving object.

Each successive orbit brought Sputnik I a trifle closer to the earth and into denser air (Fig. 5). Even though this air was a billion times less dense than that which we breathe at sea level, its repeated braking effect upon the satellite caused it to sink slowly into the vast ocean of air. At last Sputnik I lost a mile a

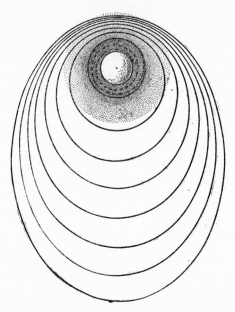

Fig. 5. Fate of a satellite is shown in these exaggerated orbits. As air resistance slows the object down, its maximum height or apogee decreases more rapidly than the perigee. Eventually its orbit becomes circular and further slowing causes it to spiral into the earth.

day in altitude and then it made its last complete pass around the world and porpoised into the lower atmosphere like a glowing meteor, disintegrating somewhere over Mongolia.

The first artificial satellite traveled a total of almost 40 million miles. Before it plunged into the lower air, it was joined in the inky darkness of earth-space by a big brother—a massive Sputnik II containing half a ton of payload. Launched on November 3, 1957, just about one month after the historic blast-off of the first artificial moon, Sputnik II had a sensational impact upon the world. Sputnik II, described as a "flying laboratory," was placed into orbit at an altitude of 140 miles, very close to the perigee of its predecessor, but it whirled outward to a maximum distance of 1,038 miles. It took 102 minutes to complete a single trip around this exaggerated elliptical race track in space.

Laika, a little Husky dog, was a passenger aboard Sputnik II. She was strapped inside a specially outfitted, pressurized cabin where she was provided with a controlled atmosphere and periodically fed food and water. Russian scientists revealed that Laika had undergone months of training to prepare her for her entry into space. She was conditioned to endure the cramped quarters and strange environment without violent reaction. Laika was fitted with special instruments designed to record physiological data such as her respiration and heartbeat.

An official report describes part of Laika's reaction to her heroic ride:

The behavior and condition of the animal during the sputnik's ascent to the orbit was registered quite fully. The information obtained indicates that the animal withstood the increase in its seeming weight and continued to move its head and body freely only until a certain point of the acceleration. After that the animal was pressed to the floor of the chamber and no more or less noticeable movements were registered.

A study of the data obtained from the sputnik showed that immediately after launching, the frequency of the heart contractions approximately trebled as compared with the initial frequency. The electrocardiograms have not revealed any morbid symptoms. . . . Later on when the effect of the acceleration not only continued but mounted, the heart-beat frequency diminished.

When Laika settled down into orbit and became the first weightless dog in history, she apparently did not mind her unusual conditions of life. According to official reports, Laika behaved "moderately" and breathed "normally." She was fed routinely by an automatic device until she died sometime within the first week. Details of her demise are not available; she may have died from a lack of oxygen or, more humanely, from a fatal poison.

Whatever the cause of Laika's death, there was to be no post-mortem. Sputnik II hurtled through orbital space until on April 14, 1958, chariot and passenger alike dove into the lower atmosphere and came to an incandescent end. Tumbling end over end the satellite finished its 2369th orbit by passing over Long Island at an altitude of 80 miles. It was last sighted 40 miles east of Trinidad and probably ended up somewhere near the mouth of the Amazon.

The Soviets have revealed nothing about the nature of the rocket boosters which permitted them to place Sputniks I and II in orbit, but it was not difficult to deduce that they were using their huge ICBM for this purpose and that it had a thrust of about 800,000 pounds. Furthermore, from the orbital data our scientists could calculate something about the accuracy of the Soviet ICBM. They concluded that Soviet guidance capability was sufficient to place an ICBM warhead within two miles of its target.

The deductions about Soviet thrust and guidance had the most chilling military significance. The conclusion was inescapable that the Soviet Union was well on its way to building up a militarily effective ICBM striking force. By leapfrogging its technology the Soviet Union apparently planned to number the days of the manned bomber and put its faith in the long-range rocket.

But to many the significance of the October-November launchings transcended the military implications. This was well phrased by the U.S. Information Agency director, George V. Allen:

Probably the most significant result of the Soviet successes is a change in the overall impression of the people of the world about the Soviet Union. In public opinion parlance, we speak of this as the revised Soviet image. The change goes beyond the field of space technology. It covers all of Soviet science and technology, plus Soviet military power and general standing.

Before Sputnik I, few people of the free world believed the Soviet was currently in a position to challenge America in the broad fields of science, technology, and production. Now the Sputniks . . . are taken as evidence that the Soviet Union is able to challenge America successfully in all these fields, including even production.

It is hardly an overstatement to say that space has become for many people the primary symbol of world leadership in all areas of science and technology.

The earth-circling satellites had deep military and political significance, but I am of the mind that they had a deeper symbolism. I believe that they appealed to many men as symbolizing a momentous time of change—an inflexion point in history. Throughout all his life on this planet, man had been chained to earth and his efforts focused on things close at hand. The gravity-defying Sputnik gave new dimension to man's life. Suddenly his thoughts were directed upward and outward. Man had begun his journey to the stars and the prospects enthralled people everywhere.

A number of U.S. scientists and government officials were dismayed that the Soviets had beaten us into space. They urged that Project Vanguard be speeded up. Others, like Dr. Wernher von Braun, fumed that they had not been given a chance to send a satellite into orbit. Working for the U.S. Army at its Huntsville, Alabama, ballistic missile installation, von Braun had been trying for over two years to win approval for a satellite project. Although he had been turned down repeatedly, he never gave up trying to persuade Defense Department officials that his group should be given authority for an orbital mission. Finally, on the night that Sputnik I went into orbit, von Braun got "one of those little psychological breaks that happen only a couple of times or once in a lifetime"—to use the words of General John B. Medaris, officer in charge of the Army Ballistic Missile Agency. It so happened that Neil McElroy, newly appointed as Secretary of Defense, was making a tour of military installations and stayed overnight at Huntsville.

Dr. von Braun buttonholed Defense Secretary McElroy and briefed him upon the satellite capability of Army ballistic missiles like the intermediate-range Jupiter. He explained that he had made formal overtures to the Pentagon, seeking permission for a satellite project, and despite the fact that he had promised to get a satellite in orbit by January 1, 1957, his requests had been denied. Von Braun was confident that his Huntsville team could put a satellite in orbit within 60 days after the project was authorized. The Defense Secretary promised to look into the matter and on November 8 the Huntsville project was officially approved.

Meanwhile the Vanguard I rocket was being rushed to completion and on Dec. 6, 1957, it stood on its launch pad at Cape Canaveral, Florida, ready for the countdown on the first U.S. missile to attempt orbital flight. Two seconds after the main engine was ignited, the Vanguard I lost thrust and was consumed in a mass of flame. America's first contestant in the space race had flunked out. No second Vanguard stood on the launch pad at Cape Canaveral ready to back up our first attempt at a space shot. In retrospect, it is difficult to imagine a more disastrous comparison between the technological efforts of the two great world powers.

Sputniks I and II were still in orbit while Dr. von Braun and his Huntsville team readied their missile for its premier performance. Known as Explorer I, the satellite package consisted of a six-inch-diameter tube 80 inches in length. This case contained the last-stage propellant, 13 pounds of solid fuel, which was a rubber-base type of powder specially developed for rocket propulsion. The satellite itself weighed 18 pounds, certainly not an impressive statistic when placed along side the tenfold heavier payload of Sputnik I, not to mention the even more massive Sputnik II package. But in its forced-draft attempt to orbit something, the United States had to take advantage of a reliable launch vehicle. This was the Army's Jupiter-C, a research vehicle built to explore re-entry of ballistic nose cones for military missiles. On September 20, 1956, Jupiter-C had been successfully fired to an altitude of 680 miles and over a range of 3,300 miles. The first stage of this Army missile consisted of a rocket casing 70 inches in diameter and 57 feet in height. It was powered by a Redstone engine (named after Redstone Arsenal at Huntsville) which some of the V-2 experts, imported into the U.S.A., developed as the power plant for an Army missile of intermediate range. The second and third stages atop the massive first stage were both solid-fuel rockets adapted from another Army missile, Sergeant. The fourth and last stage, which we have already described, towered on top of this assembly.

On the last day of January, 1958, Jupiter-C was fired successfully with all stages performing according to plan. Jupiter-C hurled its upper stages to high altitude and the final stages of the rocket successively boosted the payload to the required orbital speed. The upper stages were spun on the missile axis by means of electric motors so that they were stabilized in flight —as a bullet is given a spin when it is fired through a grooved barrel. Explorer I arced into orbit, ranging from a perigee of 224 miles to an apogee of 1,573 miles.

Von Braun was elated that the satellite shot had been successful only 83 days after the go-ahead had been given for the project. The Jupiter-C, with its thrust of 83,000 pounds, had proved to be a reliable launch vehicle. However, Dr. Von Braun's joy was tempered by the realization that the U.S. space première of January 31, 1958, could have taken place more than a year earlier. As the German missile pioneer said, with reference to the Redstone firing of a three-stage missile on September 20, 1956: "Had we replaced the 84-pound payload of this missile by a fourth stage, as we later did with the Explorers, this same missile would have been able to orbit. Thus the earliest possible date would have been September, 1956."

Even if the United States had listened to space enthusiasts and beaten the Soviets into space, it could not have made up for the lack of thrust in its vehicle launchers. Development of rocket engines and vehicles is time-consuming; Redstone, for example, was started in 1950. Referring to the satellites which the U.S. launched in 1958, Dr. von Braun observed: "Our little Explorers and Vanguards are competing with the Sputniks in spirit only. But in terms of rocket hardware they are no match."

American scientists applied their ingenuity to cramming as much scientific equipment into their small satellites as they could and they were very successful in discovering much about earth-space in early rocket experiments. But they were handicapped by the thrust gap and by the associated limitation of payload weight which could be injected into orbit. This deficiency was to plague U.S. efforts in the space contest well into the '60's.

4

THE U.S. SPACE
PROGRAM

HISTORIANS who survey the evolution of the U.S. space
program will note the confusion on the intercontinental ballistic
missile, the lack of civilian-military co-ordination in utilizing
military missiles for space applications and the failure of national
leaders to appreciate the global impact of the space race. They
will observe in retrospect that when the United States did
announce its satellite project in the summer of 1955, it made
cautious, but well-advertised, technical overtures to the challenge of space. Once the Soviet breakthrough in space occurred,
historians will record, the U.S. government took time to appreciate the significance of the event.

Many highly placed U.S. officials, including those in the
White House, seemed insensitive to the Soviet challenge. A great
hue and cry, originating in the American press and translated

into congressional pressure, forced the Administration to take a new look at its space activities and at its organization for the conduct of space research. The success of Explorer I was presented as evidence that the United States was not lagging too far behind the Soviets.

Explorer I may be taken as a good example of the twofold nature of the space race. From a scientific viewpoint this 18-pound satellite was eminently successful. Instruments aboard the first U.S. space device recorded measurements of temperature, meteoritic impact and penetrating radiation. Data taken by these devices were coded in radio messages which were telemetered down to a network of earth stations where radio receivers picked up the signals. Scientists then decoded the relayed information and analyzed it for its scientific value.

Dr. James A. Van Allen, the personable chairman of the physics department at the University of Iowa, was the key man in a research team which studied the radiation data sent back by Explorer I. The 44-year-old physicist, who had worked for the Navy during the war, turned his attention to rocket research and pioneered in designing compact instruments which could be fitted into the nose cones of high-altitude sounding rockets. Dr. Van Allen persevered in seeking measurements of cosmic rays, the mysterious and penetrating rays which come in from outer space, even though results of a few minutes of rocket data were often distressingly meager. Furthermore, the high-altitude rockets never rose high enough to give results about radiation in the 500-to-1,000-mile altitude bracket. This was unexplored territory and no one knew prior to Explorer I what one would find there.

As Explorer I looped its way around the earth, swinging in huge ellipses out to 1,573 miles above our planet, it registered the intensity of penetrating atomic particles and relayed this information back to earth. Analyzing the vast collection of data, Dr. Van Allen and his colleagues were astonished to find that at certain distances the number of rays hitting the satellite was extremely high. Yet, closer to and farther from earth the intensity dropped off. Further analysis showed that the radiation appeared to be confined to a belt stretching around the earth's girth like a huge inner tube. Van Allen's name has been given to this radiation belt around the earth. The Van Allen belt first discovered is centered about 2,000 miles above sea level. A second Van Allen belt, discovered later, lies farther from the earth and has a complex form stretching farther north and south. The shape of these belts and the nature of the radiation still remain to be investigated thoroughly, but it is clear that the discovery of such concentrations of what appear to be electrons and charged hydrogen atoms, or protons, is of major scientific importance. The radiation belts are sufficiently intense that they may form a biological hazard in near-earth space travel.

Thus Explorer I, which is still in orbit although its radio transmitters are silent, turned in a first-rate scientific performance. And the United States geared itself to expanding its space science program. President Eisenhower said on April 2, 1958, that there were four factors giving "urgency and inevitability to advancement in space technology." These he listed as:

(1) The compelling urge of man to explore the unknown;
(2) The need to assure that full advantage is taken of the military potential of space;
(3) The effect on national prestige of accomplishment in space science and exploration;
(4) The opportunities for scientific observation and experimentation which will add to our knowledge of the earth, the solar system and the universe.

President Eisenhower listed these factors in a message to the Congress urging the creation of a new National Aeronautics and Space Agency for administering the civilian space science and exploration program. Looking over the four reasons given for "going into space," exempting the military value, we see that there emerge two basic motivations for a civilian space program. There are only two because reasons (1) and (4) coalesce. Summing up, the two reasons are: first, scientific research and exploration; and, second, enhancement of national prestige.

I think it important to make these two distinctions because unless we understand the objective we will fail to build a program suitable for its attainment. The duality of the motivation unfortunately translates into different technical objectives and space programs. In effect, it means that there are two space races being run concurrently—the scientific program and the prestige program. Explorer I could scarcely be considered anything but an also-ran in the prestige race.

By the time that the Congress received the President's message, it had already held exhaustive hearings on the space problem and it was genuinely concerned that the U.S. was lagging in the space field. Congressmen sought the advice of scientists, administrators, military leaders and elder statesmen. The Congress was addressing itself to a new field of human endeavor. Politicians (there is not a single physical scientist in the Congress) needed to be educated and they listened patiently to experts, who at times might have been talking Greek as far as the congressmen were concerned. But many of the witnesses, such as the Washington-wise Dr. Lloyd Berkner, were able to talk the language of the laymen. Dr. Berkner, a Navy veteran and key scientist in the International Geophysical Year, was deeply impressed by the Sputniks. Referring to them he told the congressmen:

Thus we are daily reminded that on October 4, 1957, man made his first escape from his imprisonment on the surface of planet earth. Even more than nuclear energy, the satellite symbolizes the cohesive force of science in bringing together and cementing political, social, and economic elements of man's civilization. For it shows us science, not as a thing apart from man's daily activities but as all-pervading force, that influences every aspect of human existence—not just man's material welfare, nor his political and military posture, but his humor, literature and poetry as well. In acquiring his newly won, three-dimensional freedom he is reminded that he enjoys greater opportunity than the simple material existence of the ant-hill—an opportunity for curiosity, exploration, and comprehension—the intellectual power that makes man more than the ant.

Dr. Berkner asserted: "As a simple scientific tool, the instrumented earth satellite is a device of superb potentialities, comparable to such other great scientific instruments as the telescope, microscope or nuclear accelerator. It provides access to the secrets of our environment that can be acquired in no other way."

"But above all," Dr. Berkner summed up, "the man-made satellite provides the first step towards man's dream of interplanetary travel, a dream that is now almost realized. Over and above the adventure itself, and quite apart from the unevaluated advantages of occupying other planets, the scientific knowledge to be acquired in such exploration is prodigious. That there are some forms of life on Mars, for example, seems quite certain. The difference in the evolutionary patterns under presumably independent circumstances could easily provide basic keys to the origin of life itself."

Congressmen, listening to the erudite counsel of scientists and hearing matter-of-fact references to trips to the moon and to Mars, and references to the origin of life, must have been jolted by the testimony. Discussions of orbital vehicles, spaceships and interplanetary communication were a far cry from the usual business of the legislators. I attended quite a few of the space hearings and I discussed many of the problems with congressmen, both young and old. Most admitted that they found it difficult to comprehend the dimensions of the space problem, but they felt the urgency of "catching up with the Russians." They were less concerned with pure or basic research, which gave little prospect of practical pay-off. And some congressmen worried over the military potential of space.

H. G. Wells made some fantastic predictions about man and space in *The War of the Worlds,* so it was natural that there should be concern about the military use of space. On this

THE U.S. SPACE PROGRAM 43

score, Dr. Simon Ramo, a leading space expert and a top missile man, tended to debunk the military value of space. He pointed out that "putting our H-bombs out in space or on the moon, with the necessary means for assuring that they will come down when desired to the right place, looks like a different but poorer way of doing it. Outer space is new, but so is the bottom of the ocean; this does not mean that we should put our retaliatory forces there." Despite this assurance, the thought of H-bombs circulating in orbit is a chilling one.

The Defense Department did have a legitimate stake in the satellite field. There was a military requirement for orbital devices that could perform communications and reconnaissance missions. The orbiting of Sputniks I and II caused the military satellite program to be given a high priority. Furthermore, the development of the Atlas ICBM with its 360,000-pound thrust gave the Defense Department the potential of boosting heavier payloads into space when the new rocket became operational. Naturally, the reconnaissance or "spy" satellite program was highly classified. This fact, together with the military secrecy attached to ICBM rockets which would be used for civilian applications, added complexity to the emergency U.S. space program.

A purely peacetime civilian space activity could be conducted most effectively and most efficiently if all details of the work could be kept unclassified. Furthermore, international co-operation would be facilitated by nonsecret research. Unfortunately, it seemed, even space science was to have two antipodal aspects.

In one respect, it seemed that the new U.S. space agency would have a clear field, unfettered by military bonds. The Pentagon saw no need for spaceships or for the huge rocket engines needed to power them. This was to prove a lucky break for the civilian space program, even though it later developed that there could be military applications for very high-thrust rockets.

As if to underscore the tempo of the space race and to dramatize their rocket superiority, the Soviets shot Sputnik III into orbit on May 15, 1958. Congressmen who were pondering the organization of the new space agency were greatly impressed with the mammoth satellite. Plate 1 illustrates the complexity of the device, which measured six feet at its base and was almost 12 feet in length. Sputnik III weighed 2,925 pounds and contained an array of automatic instruments for measuring and telemetering data on orbital space. The massive satellite was sent into an orbital ellipse almost identical to that of Sputnik II, attesting to the superb marksmanship of Soviet rocket experts. It was clear that the Soviets were deeply committed to a vigorous space program. In addition, they were concentrating upon heavy payloads which could be lifted into space by their overpowered ICBM boosters.

Congressional committees investigating the space problem heard two and a half million words of testimony. This great outflowing of words took place after Sputnik II and concluded in the spring of 1958. These were, of course, not the last words on space, since the Congress established two special committees to watch over space developments, but they served to end the debate on how the U.S. should organize its new Space Agency. Early in the summer of the same year, the Congress passed the Space Act of 1958 and established the National Aeronautics and Space Administration (NASA).

NASA was formally in business on October 1, 1958, not quite a full year after Sputnik I ushered in the space age. The new Space Agency (many still use the name that President Eisenhower gave it) inherited all the facilities and personnel of the National Advisory Committee on Aeronautics (NACA). This was both a plus and a minus on the balance sheet. On one hand it put NASA in business with a going organization; on the other, it encumbered the new agency with the barnacles and deadwood of an old-line government bureau. NACA was set up in 1915 and, while it did succeed in making some significant contributions to aircraft design, it was scarcely geared to the pace of the space age. NACA personnel assumed positions of high rank in NASA along with key men from the Vanguard program; the combination did little to raise hope that the U.S. would formulate a truly aggressive space program. For one thing NACA preferred to do its own research and development in its own laboratories and centers, rather than contract out work to independent groups in industry or in educational institutions. NACA had a staff of 8,000 employees located at the Lewis Laboratory (Cleveland, Ohio), at Langley Field (Virginia) and at Moffett Field (California).

Dr. T. Keith Glennan was picked by President Eisenhower to be the first administrator for NASA. A former Atomic Energy Commissioner and president of Case Institute of Technology, Dr. Glennan was assigned the formidable task of guiding the civilian aspects of the U.S. space effort. Had he been forced to tackle this assignment with only the scientific resources of NACA and Vanguard, Dr. Glennan would have faced an unenviable chore. NASA acquired a most valuable asset in the form of the Jet Propulsion Laboratory at the California Institute of Technology. JPL, as it was called, made 2,600 employees available to NASA (others work on defense projects). Most important was the fact that an imaginative and resourceful scientist, Dr. William H. Pickering, headed up the laboratory. The JPL addition gave the new space agency an impressive boost in the important field of rocket fuel and engine development.

But NASA needed more than a rocket research facility. It urgently required a facility where it could push the development and construction of high-thrust rockets which could compete with the payload capability of Soviet Sputniks. Here it had a double stroke of good luck. Not only had the Defense Department launched a rocket project of this kind; it was apparently willing to transfer the facility to NASA. There was no unanimity on initial willingness to hand over the Defense project because there were those who felt very strongly (and they still do) that there was a military requirement for large space vehicles.

Juno V was the name given to the Defense Department's

project for building big rocket boosters. The program had originated in the early summer of 1958 as several scientist-advisors in the Pentagon decided that there was a military need for a 1.5-million-pound-thrust booster. Dr. von Braun and his Huntsville rocket experts were intrigued with the idea of developing a massive booster. It fitted in with von Braun's dreams of building a huge spaceship. He felt that the immense rocket could be developed most quickly if a cluster of eight separate engines were used for the first stage. This project was started at Huntsville and was later given the code name Saturn and transferred to NASA.

An additional facility known as the High Speed Flight Station at Edwards Air Force Base was annexed by NASA. This base, located in the Mojave Desert about 100 miles north of Los Angeles, is the test center for the experimental X-15 rocket plane. The X-15 is a research project of the Air Force, Navy and NASA designed to collect aerodynamic data on free flight of an experimental plane. A sequel to the X-15 is a flight vehicle known as the Dynasoar Project. It is a hypersonic, winged orbital vehicle designed for global flights. Dynasoar differs from a true satellite in that it is designed to skip around the fringe of the earth's atmosphere like a flat stone sent skimming over water. The earth-circling orbital vehicle is largely an Air Force project but its success may be linked to the use of large NASA boosters to propel the military craft into orbital space. Air Force experts estimate that the development of Dynasoar will cost $1 billion and will not be completed until 1965. The Dynasoar is in reality a space glider which the military hope will be able to conduct global missions and return safely to a military base.

NASA also acquired the Pilotless Aircraft Station at Wallops Island, Virginia, along with the naval station at Chincoteague, Virginia, where small and medium-sized experimental rockets are launched. The major launch site for NASA vehicles is the Atlantic Missile Range at Cape Canaveral, Florida. NASA shares facilities with the Defense Department, using ICBM launch pads for its space launchings. Independent launch complexes are being built for NASA's most ambitious projects which require special ground environment such as oversize fuel tanks, assembly buildings and test towers.

All in all, the fledgling space enterprise appropriated a considerable number of facilities at which to concentrate its research and development projects. NASA also acquired 553 acres of land from the Department of Agriculture's Beltsville, Maryland, station. It selected this site, almost in the shadow of the Capitol, for building its huge Goddard Space Flight Research Center. Some 2,000 employees are assigned the mission of masterminding satellite projects, including Project Mercury for orbiting a man in space, as well as many other satellite plans.

The Goddard Center is named in honor of the great U.S. rocket pioneer, Dr. Robert H. Goddard. The American rocket expert filed over 200 patents for rocket and jet-propulsion inventions which he made during the 1930-41 period. Goddard used the experimental approach to rocketry whereas his Russian counterpart Tsiolkovski focused upon theoretical aspects of the embryonic science.

NASA's accomplishments during its first few years were limited by the need to consolidate its organizational structure, by competition with the Defense Department for launch vehicles and facilities and by a lack of over-all planning. Needless to say, NASA could not equal the weight-lifting ability of Soviet rockets, so U.S. satellites were relatively small in weight. These may not have been impressive in the race for space prestige but they served to demonstrate the potential utility of satellites in near-earth space. American scientists and technologists adopted the practice of microminiaturization to make small satellites do the work of many-fold larger payloads. The new technique of microminiaturizing equipment was possible because of the new electronic devices, like transistors, which required very little electrical power.

During 1958 NASA space experiments concentrated upon Explorer and Vanguard satellites. The year was marked by nine failures, but U.S. successes included three Explorers, two

Pioneers and one Vanguard. Explorer III extended investigations of the Van Allen radiation belt and provided valuable information about the frequency of micrometeorite, or cosmic dust, impacts in space. Explorer IV carried a heavier payload of 26 pounds and relayed back to earth more data about the radiation belts. The Vanguard program, which was bedeviled by all manner of setbacks, finally got off the ground and Vanguard I orbited with a perigee of 409 miles and an apogee of 2,453 miles. Vanguard I performed nobly despite its tiny size (6.4 inches in diameter; weight: 3.25 pounds) and because of its high perigee it is expected to remain in orbit for hundreds of years.

Vanguard I carried two different kinds of power supplies. One consisted of lightweight mercury batteries which failed after a few weeks and the other was a new type of solar battery which is expected to last indefinitely. In fact, the Vanguard I radio is still transmitting faithfully. The solar battery is ideal for space applications since solar energy is free and available as long as the satellite does not get in the shadow of a planet. Even in this case, the solar cells are useful since the energy absorbed when in sunlight can be stored in batteries to carry the satellite over until it emerges into sunlit space.

A solar cell is simply a thin disk of silicon—the chief element in sand—which is specially treated on one surface so that when sunlight strikes it, the energy is absorbed and an electrical current flows through the cell. In other words, a solar cell is a trap for catching the energy in sunlight. A solar battery is nothing more than a series of such cells joined together so as to provide more electricity. The solar devices are only about ten percent efficient, but this is enough so that a square yard of cells joined together furnishes about 100 watts of electrical power —enough to light a bright household lamp and more than enough for many satellites where power requirements have been trimmed by reliance upon transistors.

Pioneer I was a bold attempt to go deeper into space with a 39-pound scientific payload. Launched on October 11, 1958, by means of a first stage Thor (an intermediate-range military missile) and Vanguard upper stages, the payload was aimed at exploring lunar space. Called a lunar probe, the vehicle streaked about 70,000 miles into space and then plunged back to earth, disappearing somewhere in the Pacific area. Pioneer I, despite its 43-hour life, obtained some useful data on the earth's magnetic field and on the radiation belt.

The U.S. space spectacular of 1958 came shortly before Christmas when an Atlas (Project Score) put a 150-pound payload, along with a two-ton final stage, or missile carcass, into an elliptical orbit. Automatic equipment in the satellite broadcast to earth a message from President Eisenhower; this was the first time that a human voice was beamed in from space.

NASA extended its Vanguard, Explorer and Pioneer experiments during 1959, using payloads of about 100 pounds. Ten civilian missile launchings were attempted and five were classed as successful. The United States was challenged early in 1959 when the Soviets shot a space probe (Lunik I) past the moon into a solar orbit. Again it was a heavyweight space device estimated to weigh 3,245 pounds. Lunik I—or Mechta, as the Soviets called it, meaning "dream"—plunged past the moon and went into a solar orbit. It continues to circle the sun with a period of 15 months; its transmitters are now dead.

Vanguard II, put into a wide elliptical orbit on February 17, 1959, was a U.S. attempt to do cloud-cover studies. Although the payload orbited on a good trajectory, the satellite developed a wobbling motion which confused the quality of the observations. Pioneer IV, a 13.4 pound lunar probe, went somewhat wide of the moon, missing it by 37,000 miles, and then went into an eternal solar orbit. The lunar probe was accelerated to 24,790 miles per hour (188 mph less than planned) for its mission. Its closest approach to the sun (perihelion) is 91,700,-000 miles and its farthest swing (aphelion) takes it 106,100,000 miles from the sun. Pioneer IV established a record in that it was tracked by radio signals out to a distance of 407,000 miles.

On August 7, 1959, the United States sent its first paddle-wheel satellite into an extreme elliptical orbit. The name derives from the four paddle-shaped vanes (Plate 2) jutting out from the satellite spheroid; these are the banks of solar cells, 8,000 in all, that supply electrical power to nickel-cadmium chemical storage batteries which are the power supply for Explorer VI. Injected into orbit at an altitude of 156 miles, Explorer VI ranged out to a distance of 26,357 miles. The payload of 142 pounds was packed with compact electronic gadgets for measuring a variety of earth-space characteristics.

If one judged the status of the space race purely in terms of the orbital population, then the United States was superior to the Soviet Union. On the other hand, if one assayed the contest in terms of sheer weight of payloads shot into orbit, then the Soviets enjoyed a long lead. On the basis of published scientific information, the U.S. scored heavily over Soviet competition. For example, within a few months after the receipt of the data from space, Dr. Van Allen was sending impressive scientific reports to 66 nations participating in the International Geophysical Year program. By contrast, the Soviets clamped tight secrecy over their rockets, never once releasing a photograph of a launching. Moreover, the Russian scientists were slow in making their data available to the scientific community. However, the Soviets were not sluggish about releasing propaganda about their space spectaculars nor were they bashful about using space rockets for their political value. To illustrate the point, Lunik II was launched on September 12, 1959. On September 13, at 5 P.M. Eastern Daylight Time, Lunik scored a hit on the moon. At noon on September 15, Premier Khrushchev touched down on U.S. soil, bringing souvenirs of Lunik II, to begin his tour of the U.S.A.

We cannot tally the satellite census of 1959 without adding six additional U.S. devices called Discoverers. These military orbital gadgets represented a firing of nine Thor boosters. Meant to explore the problems involved in developing a practical orbital reconnaissance vehicle, the Discoverers were shot in polar orbits and attempts were made to eject and recover a

300-pound capsule from the device. No recoveries were successful in 1959 but the Air Force continued its efforts in a series of
38 planned launchings. A separate chapter is devoted to military
space vehicles, but it is pertinent to add here that the Defense
Department played a large role in U.S. space achievements.
Explorers III and IV, Project Score and lunar shots originated
with the military establishment. During the first two years of
the space age, the military space program had about the same
budget as NASA.

Specific space developments during 1960 are described in the
chapters which follow and they are included as part of the 10-
year program of future space research which NASA announced
in 1960. The highlights and broad scope of this 10-year civilian
space effort appear below; the details are discussed later.

The NASA program for 1960-70, as revealed on July 28,
1960, lists the following highlights:

1961   The first U.S. manned, orbital flight (Project Mercury).
Testing of new U.S. space vehicle (Atlas-Centaur).
First U.S. lunar impact experiment. Close-up television of the
moon (Project Ranger).
Weather reconnaissance missions (Project Nimbus).

1962   Interplanetary probes to Mars and Venus (Project Mariner).
Survey of lunar surface by television.
Launching of 1,000-pound scientific satellites.

1963   Lunar "soft" landing with 600-pound payload (Project Sur-
veyor).
Orbiting of geophysical observatory.
Test of two-stage Saturn.

1964   3,500-pound astronomical observatory in earth orbit.
Unmanned reconnaissance flights to Mars and Venus.
Test of three-stage Saturn.
Unmanned lunar circumnavigation and return to earth.

1965   Planetary orbiters—to Mars and Venus (Project Voyager).
Lunar survey by unmanned mobile vehicles (Project Pros-
pector).
Begin six Saturn launchings per year.

	Test of nuclear rocket stage (Project Rover).
1966	Establishment of permanent earth-station in orbit.
to	Remote microscopy of lunar samples.
1969	Recovery of lunar samples.
	Launching of Nova-type vehicle.
	Manned circumlunar missions (Project Apollo).

Beyond
1970   Manned missions to moon and return to earth.

This NASA timetable for space exploits becomes fuzzy in the period after 1965 because it is difficult to predict the incubation time for basic research upon which these long-range experiments depend. Naturally, any projection of things to come in space must be keyed to the level of effort which one plans to make in the future. This, in turn, usually means—especially to the Congress—how much money will be spent. The annual budget at the beginning of the sixties was approximately $1 billion. In estimating the cost of the NASA space program for a full decade, Dr. Glennan stated that it would run "somewhere between $12 and $15 billion" and that an annual rate of $1.5 billion would be reached.

NASA's ten-year plans include the launching of 260 vehicles of which 62 launchings will be aimed at perfecting the vehicle, 41 will relate to manned space flight missions, 96 will focus upon scientific satellites, 28 will be concentrated upon satellite applications and the remaining 33 will be allocated to lunar and planetary missions. Vehicle development, production and launching constitute the big items in the U.S. civilian space budget.

From the scientist's viewpoint the NASA plans for this decade exceed anything which he would have expected a few short years ago. The program of space exploration is a real bonanza. The data already coming in from space, plus the torrent of new information that will flow from experiments now planned, are certain to form a priceless treasure chest for science. Yet few scientists are so naïve as to suppose that these billions of dollars will be spent for adding to the joy of the researcher. It is, of course, academic to ask how much money would be spent in the decade were the Soviet scientists not competing with us. I suspect that the amount would be far less than the $12 to $15 billion that Dr. Glennan estimated.

Granted that we are not spending or planning to spend these billions for the sake of science, but rather for attaining prestige through space feats, does the 10-year NASA program assure space supremacy for America? We have no foreknowledge of the Soviet time schedule but if we look at the impressive "firsts" scored by the Soviets in the initial years of the space competition, it seems unlikely that their space program will slow its tempo.

If the Soviets are the first to send astronauts around the moon, the first to man a huge earth satellite, the first to land on the moon, then the world will appraise the American space effort as second best. For myself, I find that the 10-year U.S. space program is adequate scientifically, but I do not believe that it is truly competitive with the Russians in the real space race. The penalty for starting so poorly in the contest is that now we must make up for the lost years; this inevitably means an accelerated program and a doubling and a tripling of the space budget.

5

MAN IN ORBIT

THE SOVIETS probably began planning for orbiting a man in space prior to Sputnik I. They took full advantage of their superior rocket thrust to hurl massive satellites into earth orbits. When they launched two five-ton spacecraft into orbit in 1960 —and successfully recovered animals from ejected space capsules —they demonstrated that they had achieved the technical capability of manned orbital flight.

In the United States, intensive planning for putting men into orbit began early in 1958. The Defense Department requested $50 million for the purpose of developing "the capability for getting a man into space and getting him back," to use the explanation given by Dr. Herbert F. York. The chief space-science advisor in the Pentagon justified the budget request:

The purpose of the program, the short-term purpose of the program is to find out what are the capabilities of man for doing useful work in the space environment. That is, under conditions of free fall, a man in a space vehicle feels as if he is falling all the time.

Now an interesting question is this: Can a man, in such a state, actually do useful work, does he simply become frantic and become incapable of doing useful work?

The U.S. man-in-space program had no great urgency during its early days. In fact, the military program which the Air Force scheduled for manned space flight was linked to Project Discoverer, which in turn was designed to orbit and recover small reconnaissance payloads. The "useful work" that astronauts might do in space was a long way in the future.

With the establishment of NASA in the autumn of 1958, there arose the vexing problem of finding some project that would show the world—not to mention the Congress—that the U.S. was not lagging in the space field. On October 5, 1958, NASA assumed responsibility for the man-in-space or Mercury Project and on April 27, 1959, President Eisenhower approved a DX or 0.01 national priority rating, putting the project on a par with the development of Atlas and Titan ICBM's. Thus one was justified in concluding that the Administration believed that it was as important to put a man in orbit as it was to perfect intercontinental ballistic missiles.

George M. Low, chief of NASA's manned-space-flight program, revealed that: "Project Mercury was conceived, and is being carried out, in a manner that will attempt to achieve manned orbital flight at the earliest practicable date." In the transition of the man-in-space program from the Air Force to NASA, it suddenly became a project of the highest urgency and this fact must inevitably be explained by the insertion of "earliest practicable date" which NASA defined for its Project Mercury. It is significant that Air Force Project 7969, "Manned Ballistic Rocket Research System," which antedated Project Mercury and which was, in fact, its precursor, enjoyed no such priority and was handicapped by a lack of funds.

NASA proceeded to ask the Congress for $100 million to support Project Mercury, but by 1960 it was clear that it would require at least four times this amount before an American astronaut would be in orbit. The priority and the funds assigned to Project Mercury puzzled many scientists. The scientific and technological rewards promised by Project Mercury did not justify focusing such effort upon it. It was apparent that the work was being undertaken on a crash basis as a concentrated effort to chalk up a spectacular "first" in space. There could be no doubt of the publicity value of a première orbital flight attended by the successful recovery of the astronaut. But the Soviets had a head start in space and had the undeniable advantage of high thrust with which to boost massive satellites into orbit. Furthermore, Soviet rocket achievements of the first few years following Sputnik I accented their reliance upon this high thrust to produce space spectaculars. Based upon past performance and probable capability, it seemed that the United States was belatedly entering into a contest with the odds against success.

No one with knowledge of rocketry expected that the world would awake without warning to find a Soviet astronaut in orbit. The initial entry of man into orbit would be preceded by a series of "dry runs," using animals and dummies as stand-ins for human beings. Furthermore, there would probably be a series of manned, ballistic flights in which a man would be projected several hundred miles above sea level and then recovered down range. Such flights in the Soviet Union could be conducted without fanfare and failures could be concealed without too much trouble. In the United States the launching of our first astronaut is likely to be a highly publicized event; in fact, a NASA official told the author that some 500 newsmen and members of the radio and television industry will attend the Mercury première at Cape Canaveral. The consequences of a failure could be disastrous. One NASA spokesman predicted: "Picture what will happen if we kill off an astronaut on the launch pad."

On May 15, 1960, a Soviet "Spacecraft, 1960 Epsilon" went into a 200-mile earth orbit. The Greek letter identifies the chronological order of the satellite. The spacecraft was a huge, five-ton vehicle commonly identified as an ESV, or Earth Satellite Vehicle. This ESV craft consisted of a pressurized cabin weighing a total of 5,512 pounds and containing 3,250 pounds of instruments. Soviet news releases stated that a "dummy" was at the controls of the spacecraft. The retrorocket (one producing thrust in a direction opposed to that of the vehicle's motion) was fired when the spacecraft was in the wrong attitude. This rocket blast, designed to slow down the spacecraft and kick it out of orbit, actually speeded up the vehicle and sent it farther away from the earth. Had a man been aboard, the results would have been fatal since he would have become a prisoner in space. He would have perished from failure of his life-support system, probably from a lack of oxygen, unless he could have actuated emergency rockets and glided back to earth.

Soviet rocket experts had better luck on August 20, 1960, when they recovered a space capsule ejected from a spacecraft similar to the one that misfired. Referred to by the American press as "Noah's Ark" because of the number of animals aboard, the space capsule landed within about six miles of the intended recovery point. A remarkable feat of spacemanship! Two dogs, Stryelka (Little Arrow) and Byelka (Squirrel), were aboard the ESV and their reactions were observed on earth through television channels. Both space dogs survived their 437,500-mile journey which took them around the world 17 times in one day. The Soviet press statement gave no details of the descent from orbit and recovery technique other than that: "The satellite space ship . . . has special thermal protection and successfully passed through the earth's atmosphere."

Manned space flight may be attained before this book appears in print. Certainly, the pace of Soviet rocket exploits justifies this assertion. Presumably the Soviets will publicize the event fully but they may not reveal many technical details of the global flight of the rocket apparatus. The problems solved by the Soviet experts are precisely the same as those faced by American technologists, so we can examine the details of orbital flight as they appear to Project Mercury personnel.

The major problems involved in orbital flight are concerned with the safety of the astronaut during the critical periods of take-off and re-entry. Once placed in orbit, the astronaut is in a relatively safe position as long as his life-support system functions properly. But during take-off and re-entry, he faces much greater hazards owing to the many failures that may occur in the propulsion, guidance and braking equipment.

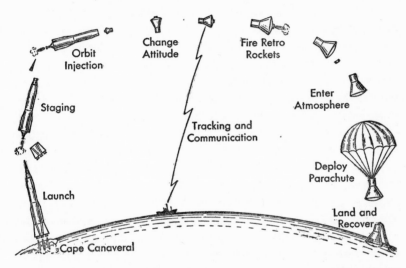

Fig. 6. Diagrammatic sketch showing various phases of the flight pattern for the Mercury capsule. *NASA*

Figure 6 depicts the various phases of the planned Mercury flight pattern. Each phase of the flight program must be completed according to schedule and provision must be made for insuring the safety of the astronauts should any part of the system fail. This necessity for building into an experimental space capsule a redundant system of safeguards greatly complicates the design of the Mercury capsule.

Preliminary contracts for the design of the Mercury capsule were drawn up in June of 1958 by the Air Force in co-operation with the National Advisory Committee on Aeronautics. NACA assigned part of the job to its Langley Research Center. When NASA took over NACA it reviewed the Mercury capsule program and drew up specifications for the orbital device. Manufacturers were invited to bid on production of the novel vehicles and twelve companies submitted final proposals on December 11, 1958. McDonnell Aircraft Corporation of St. Louis was awarded the capsule contract on February 6, 1959.

The space capsule, shown diagrammatically in Plate 3, is a hermetically sealed container made with an outer shell of nickel-cobalt alloy, an inner shell of titanium and an insulating liner to shield against cold, heat and noise. The astronaut, clad in a special pressure suit (Plate 4), is strapped into a custom-fitted couch so designed as to allow him to absorb the stress of take-off and re-entry. We will describe the outfitting of the space cabin presently, after we have looked into the preliminary events in which the astronaut or a dummy substitute will engage before the main event—orbital flight.

Many tests will be carried out with the space capsule before an astronaut takes even a short flight in one. For example, capsule models made of boiler plate, rather than expensive alloys, have been drop-tested from airplanes and also projected on ballistic trajectories by boosters. One of the important tests focused on determining whether the heat shield molded to the blunt end of the capsule would withstand the high temperatures caused by impact with the atmosphere. This heat shield consists of a glass-resin laminate, which was found to rise to a temperature of about 3,000° F. during the most crucial minute of re-entry. The blunt shape of the capsule slows the space capsule from 14,000 miles per hour to 500 mph. It was found by tests with the Atlas ICBM that the heat shield provided adequate protection for the capsule.

The program for proving out the final model of the Mercury missile is essentially a three-step sequence. First, a modest-sized rocket known as Little Joe is used to experiment with the boiler-plate capsule and check out its characteristics at low speed. Little

Joe is a solid-fuel rocket employing a cluster of four Castor and four additional Recruit rockets all of which add up to a thrust of 250,000 pounds. Little Joe rockets have been used to prove out the recovery of the capsule by means of parachute descent. In this way monkeys have been shot into space on limited excursions and successfully recovered.

The second step in the Mercury test schedule makes use of an Army rocket, the Redstone. It will be the first U.S. missile to project a man into space. To be sure, the flights will be momentary escapes from earth and at best they will free the capsule occupant from the clutch of gravity for about five minutes. During this period the gravity-defier will get the feel of weightlessness; he will do little experiments to see how well he can manipulate instruments. This will be the longest man has experienced freedom from gravity, although he has managed to achieve very short periods of weightlessness in jet planes deliberately arced so as to offset the earth's attraction.

While the challenge of space flight is largely one of getting used to weighing nothing, the problem is just the opposite on take-off and re-entry. The astronaut has to withstand the crushing burden of feeling his own body weight multiply many-fold as his space capsule accelerates and decelerates. Everyone has experienced the thrust of backward motion as an automobile is accelerated too quickly and likewise the forward push when the brakes are jammed on. In accidents when the car is stopped abruptly passengers often fly right through the windshield. And as a car takes a curve at high speed one knows that a centrifugal force is exerted. That is why modern highways are banked so as to keep the car from sliding off the road.

Centrifugal force is used to simulate the conditions of weightiness that astronauts will experience in take-off and descent. A huge merry-go-round or centrifugal machine whirls the would-be astronaut around at ever increasing speed, squeezing the man against his form-fitting couch with a force ten and even twenty times the pull of gravity. It is expected that the worst that could happen to a Mercury astronaut would amount to about 20 g's

—and this only under emergency conditions. On take-off the astronaut would probably be subjected to somewhat less than ten g's and about the same on re-entry. He will experience these crushing weights for a few moments and should be able to bear up well under the strain. Of course, if the astronaut were an aircraft pilot requiring full use of his arms and legs he would become virtually helpless under high g-forces, but the astronaut is poured into his plastic couch and has no need even to move his limbs.

Step number three will be a series of tests with full-scale payloads using Atlas missiles. The combination Atlas-Mercury dummy is called Big Joe. The rocket combination is shown in Plate 7. As the Atlas engines are ignited, three roaring streams of flame (Plate 15) spew from the rocket exhausts and thrust builds up. The Atlas is held to the launch pad by powerful restraining clamps, which are released to allow the vehicle to rise slowly into the air. At burn-out the two main engines and the base skirt drop away from the main body of the Atlas and the central or sustainer engine keeps the Atlas on its upward course. At the same time the Atlas is guided on a tilted trajectory until the missile is parallel to the earth's surface, and four minutes after take-off it is 120 miles above sea level. Small vernier (side) jets make fine adjustments in the attitude of the rocket and when the sustainer engine cuts off, they add small increments of speed to the vehicle until it attains a velocity of 17,500 mph. The Mercury capsule is then separated from the spent Atlas carcass and it glides into a circular, orbital path.

Once in orbit the Mercury capsule is held for five minutes in an attitude where the axis of the capsule makes an angle of about 40 degrees to the flight path. This is the retrofiring position. Then the capsule is reoriented by means of the jet systems shown in Fig. 6 until the angle (blunt end forward) is 14.5 degrees. This attitude allows the astronaut to see beyond the heat shield. The space capsule proceeds to make two or three orbits around the world. In its course, 17 ground stations track its path and the flight data are assembled through an elaborate communications network. These data permit computers to analyze when the command should be given to return the vehicle to earth. This command automatically reorients the rocket to retro-position and the retrorockets are fired, reducing the capsule's speed.

Firing the retrorockets subtracts about 350 mph from the speed of the Mercury capsule. This is only two per cent of its orbital speed but it is sufficient to kick the capsule out of orbit. In effect, it dramatically compresses in time and distance the gradual descent by which the satellite would normally sink into the atmosphere. Instead of a slow spiral extending around the earth many times, the Mercury capsule curves downward in a rapid trajectory over a fraction of an orbit.

The two main hazards presented to astronauts descending from orbit, assuming the timing is precise, are too-rapid deceleration and excessive heating. Both effects take place as a result of atmospheric braking. The air acts as a softly applied brake to snub the fast-moving capsule. In the case of an automobile brake, the metal-to-brake shoe contact produces frictional heat which must be dissipated by the brake drum, otherwise the brakes burn up. The Mercury capsule plunges against the resisting air with such high velocity that, even though the upper air is very thin, heat builds up on the frontal surface of the capsule. The heat generated amounts to as much as the average home in the northern U.S.A. uses during a normal winter. Experts have so designed the blunt face of the Mercury vehicle that it casts aside 99 per cent of the heat produced; this is rejected to the atmosphere. The remaining one per cent flows into the heat shield, the design of which is such that very little penetrates into the space cabin. The cabin temperature should not drop below 50° F. in orbit nor exceed 90° F. upon descent.

The initial entry of the Mercury capsule into the ocean of air takes place at a skimming angle of about two degrees. As it encounters the deeper layers of denser air, it slows down more quickly and the deceleration amounts to a nine-g force. The more the capsule bites into denser air, the more steep becomes its trajectory and, of course, the slower becomes its speed. For example, its speed should equal that of sound at an altitude of about 14 miles. When the Mercury capsule drops to subsonic speed, at an altitude of about eight miles above sea level, a small drogue parachute is deployed. This chute tends to stabilize the path of the capsule and it reduces its velocity to 200 mph. Now the capsule descends vertically and a large parachute pops out at an altitude of 10,000 feet above sea level. This lowers the vehicle to the earth below.

The performance of the Atlas-Mercury rocket will be checked out through a series of experiments over suborbital and orbital flight patterns. Primates will substitute for man in these trial runs. Additional safety features are also built into the design of the missile to allow the escape of the astronaut during the critical take-off period. For example, if catastrophe occurs on lift-off and the main Atlas fuel tanks blow up, there is an automatic abort mechanism which fires a rocket cluster attached to a tubular rigging above the Mercury capsule. Normally, this escape tower would be jettisoned after the main engines of the Atlas are discarded. In case of emergency, the thrust of the escape tower's rockets frees the capsule from the Atlas and hurls it upward out of danger. The capsule is then lowered to the ground by means of its main recovery parachute.

Assuming a successful launching and staging, the two critical factors determining the proper orbit for the satellite are the velocity at cut-off and the angle of injection. If too low a velocity is imparted to the capsule, it fails to orbit and describes a ballistic trajectory. The capsule might fall back to earth at some inaccessible spot or far from the recovery teams. Decisions must be made at very high speed in order to alter the course of the capsule by firing the retrorockets. The astronaut would be incapable of making the right decision, since he would be unable to cope with the mathematical complexity of the problem. All of the data about the flight path of the capsule have to be reviewed almost instantly by high-speed computers—which know in advance where favorable recoverable or descent areas are—

so that the capsule can be instructed properly. Even in this case, the passenger aboard the spacecraft would be an onlooker, as the instructions would be given to automatically actuated instruments and controls. Too high an orbital speed could throw the capsule into too high an altitude and thus imperil recovery. By the same token, if the angle of injection, or "lay-in," deviates too much from the horizontal, the orbital path of the Mercury capsule becomes elliptical and, again, recovery might be difficult or impossible.

The astronaut is, however, not completely helpless inside his space cabin. As he views his instrument panel he can check upon the performance of certain phases of his flight. Through his periscope he can look past the thick heat shield and view the earth below. He can turn on stabilizing jets to control the attitude of his capsule and keep it from rolling, yawing and pitching. Otherwise, he could become fearfully sick from space sickness. He can also adjust the controls governing his life-support system, so that he is assured of adequate oxygen and so that the cabin temperature is comfortable. In case of a fire in the electrical system, the astronaut can hit a valve, venting all the air from the enclosure (his oxygen face mask will keep him alive). The escape of air from the cabin produces a good vacuum and any blaze would be snuffed out in an instant; no better fire extinguisher could be desired.

The Mercuryman is in almost continuous voice contact by radio links to ground stations. He can make and transmit a few observations, but for the most part the data sent to earth stations are taken and transmitted automatically. The astronaut's reaction to space flight is measured by a variety of instruments. These transmit some of the data and record the rest on magnetic tape inside the cabin. Alone in his space capsule, the astronaut has little real privacy. He is closely watched by cameras so that his every movement and reaction is recorded.

Since the Mercury capsule is launched at an angle of 33 degrees to the Equator, it does not pass over Soviet territory—thus avoiding any controversy over intrusion into sovereign space belonging to the U.S.S.R. The trajectory passes just south of Bermuda and then crosses the Equator at the eastern edge of Africa as shown in Fig. 7. On the first circuit around the world, the southernmost point is the southwestern tip of Australia. The trajectory passes over the American land mass at Lower California (Mexico) and then slices between San Antonio and Houston, at which point some 26,000 miles is covered in one and a half hours. Should it be necessary to call the capsule down at the end of its first circuit, it may be maneuvered to land

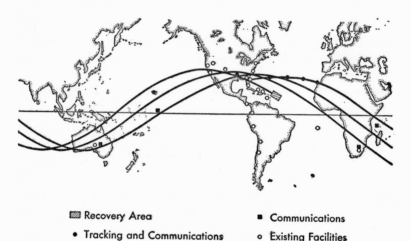

◨ Recovery Area ■ Communications
● Tracking and Communications ○ Existing Facilities

Fig. 7. Orbital flight paths for U.S. manned space missions. Launching takes place at Cape Canaveral, Florida, and recovery occurs in the shaded area as shown. *NASA*

in the recovery area. Otherwise, it continues on a second circuit and finally enters upon its third and last orbit. The Goddard Space Flight Center keeps track of the orbital path of the Mercury capsule, acting as the hub of a communications network, and it uses the data to compute the future trajectory of the satellite. Based upon computer analyses of these data, the decision is made to fire the retrorockets when the capsule is about 400 or 500 miles west of California.

The three solid-fuel jets clustered at the blunt end of the

capsule have more than enough thrust to slow the satellite down by 350 mph. Should one rocket fail, the others can take up the slack. Should the remote control signal fail; the astronaut can ignite the rockets from a cabin control. Almost imperceptibly the Mercury capsule begins its descent, passing over New Orleans while still in orbital space. Finally, somewhere close to Puerto Rico, the one-ton space device reaches the 10,000-foot altitude and a 62-foot-wide ring-sail parachute lowers the capsule to the ocean. It is dropping at 20 miles per hour when it plops into the water. Automatically operated devices cut loose the chute and release location aids so that recovery teams can find the bobbing capsule. A smoke bomb goes off, a flashing beacon begins signaling and a fluorescent dye stains the water. In addition, electronic devices, such as a radio transmitter, go into operation. Should the capsule rupture upon impact with the water, the astronaut can escape through a hatch.

This description of the Mercury satellite applies with some changes to the ESV craft designed by Soviet experts. In the case of the Soviet manned space flight, a more powerful rocket is used to propel a five-ton satellite into a higher orbit. Then a pressurized space capsule is ejected from this massive spacecraft and this is then brought to earth by atmospheric braking and finally by parachute. The Soviets employ a continental recovery area rather than a water surface.

A Soviet failure in a manned orbital flight can probably be concealed, especially if no press statements are released until after termination of the flight. The closed society of the Soviet Union grants it a great advantage in this respect. U.S. space efforts under NASA are open to public examination and are usually heralded in advance. Any manned space effort could hardly be kept secret in the United States. Should a Mercury astronaut lose his life in a space flight, there is certain to be a searching congressional inquiry. Then people might recall that some scientists were far from enthusiastic about the Mercury mission. Dr. Lee A. DuBridge, for example, warned a congressional group on April 25, 1958, that the man-in-orbit project ought to be considered most soberly. The president of the California Institute of Technology counseled:

First we must ask what the purpose of the man is. Is it simply to give him a ride for the sake of the stunt, the adventure? If so, let us be honest about it so we can then decide how much such an adventure is worth to the taxpayer.

Is the purpose of the man to operate scientific instruments, or to take scientific observations? If so, then we must ask whether unmanned scientific instruments could do the job as well for less cost. In many cases it will be found that man contributes nothing or very little.

Many rocket scientists and technologists are in favor of pursuing unmanned vehicle experiments for the present—saving the man for the time when his presence is absolutely necessary—and awaiting the time when improvements in reliability of rocket equipment will give the human passenger a better chance of returning alive.

Others argue that there is a very real difference between a man in orbit and a man in space. Project Mercury enthusiasts admit that the Mercury capsule would not be adequate for true space missions such as trips around the moon. Since the NASA timetable for space exploits puts manned circumlunar flight off until 1968, it does seem inconsistent to work on a partial solution to the problem—the return of man from orbit—when the launch date for the lunar mission is still so far in the future.

Project Mercury or its Soviet equivalent can be viewed as speeding the day when astronauts will shuttle out to orbital observatories and then return to earth. But here the limiting factor is the time required for the establishment of permanent earth satellites. Semipermanent surveillance devices may be orbited for military purposes and it is conceivable that astronauts in military uniform may be required for such satellites.

Man's first step into space, a jaunt of a few hours, marks the dawn of a new age of exploration—the beginning of exploits in space and the release of man from his ancestral planet.

6

TO THE MOON

GALILEO was the first to gaze on the moon with a power greater than that of the naked eye. Through his crude telescope he looked at the great, flat *maria,* at the craggy mountain ranges and at the multitude of crater rims which pock the moonscape. Galileo puzzled over the origin of these lunar features. Scientists today can see much more detail on the moon since they have powerful telescopes but, even so, they still argue over the processes which shaped the lunar landmarks.

Lunar authorities, such as Professor Harold Urey, ascribe the dark, gray *maria* to lava flows which—and here the experts disagree—come from great objects colliding with the moon or from lava released from beneath the lunar surface. Some experts hold to the view that there are vast dust flows on the moon. Lacking an atmosphere, for the moon has not enough gravitational pull to retain a billionth of the earth's atmosphere, there could be no dust storms, but ingenious theories have been propounded to account for the spread of the dust.

One thing upon which all scientists agree is that the moon is an arid place, devoid of surface water. While its huge *maria* might suggest dried-up seas, the towering lunar Alps, with some peaks rising as high at Mt. Everest, show no signs of water erosion. The absence of surface water and the lack of atmosphere make a naked body of the moon. This means that the moon preserves its past unaltered by the devastating effects of rain, wind and running water. We have on the moon, when we are privileged to read it, the record of billions of years. On earth the past must be discerned—or rather guessed at—by studying a record that is mutilated by the ravages of time, by grotesque obliteration through accumulation of water-moved soil and wind-carried dust and by a vast overlay of vegetation and thick forests.

As the earth's nearest neighbor, the moon is a natural target for exploration. It is a quarter of a million miles from earth and it measures 2,160 miles from rim to rim. Over-all, the matter composing the moon is 3.3 times heavier than water, so that the moon and earth's crust are not very different in this respect. Knowing the size and mass of the moon, we can readily deduce its surface gravity as being one-sixth that of the earth, a fact which means that it will be far easier for a moonship to take off from the lunar surface than from earth. But, of course, the space-ship has to reach the moon first and, as we shall see, this is no easy matter, especially if the men landing on the moon plan to return to earth.

Trips to the moon have been dreamed about by many men since the time when they had the imagination to project their thoughts out from earth. But projecting thoughts and hurling an object to the moon are quite different matters. However, Jules Verne found it no barrier to imagining a flight to the moon in his novel *From the Earth to the Moon* published in 1865. Verne's space vehicle was a manned shell named the *Columbiad* shot from an enormous cannon buried in the soil of Florida.

Shooting anything out of a cannon involves prodigious accelerations over the length of the barrel. The Germans realized the practical limits of such projection in the *Die Pariserin* bombardment gun which lobbed shells at Paris.

The modern, multiple-stage, high-thrust rocket is the answer to Jules Verne's dreams. Reaching the moon is essentially a matter of imparting a critical velocity to an object so that it escapes from the pull of the earth. This critical speed is 25,050 miles per hour. In addition to the need for velocity, the projected object must be sent in the right direction. In other words, it must have the proper guidance. If we think of the moon's disk as a target, then the kind of accuracy attained in the military use of ICBM's allows one to hit within about 100 miles of the geographic center of the moon—assuming that the aiming point is "dead center." Closer hits require more accurate guidance and it appears that this will be of the mid-course type. That is to say, when the moonbound vehicle is in between earth and moon, it will be re-aimed by starting up a rocket engine of the Agena-B type. Redirection of the vehicle is possible by automatic guidance systems which locate themselves in space by fixing upon celestial objects, just as a mariner obtains his position by sighting on the stars. Instead of human observation and intelligence, the space-borne guidance system automatically seeks and locks on to stars. With such techniques space vehicles can be guided with high precision.

Given the requisite speed and guidance, space vehicles can be dispatched on a variety of lunar missions. The weight of the payload which can be projected from earth depends upon the available thrust at launch time and upon the number of upper stages that the mission demands. For example, a total of three stages for the entire rocket is adequate for sending a payload into a deep, elliptical orbit which passes close to the moon. A fourth stage or reuse of a previous (nondiscarded) stage would be necessary to slow down a lunar-impact payload for a "soft" landing. A fifth stage would be essential to arrange for the return to earth of a space vehicle soft-landed upon the moon. The more stages which comprise a rocket, the smaller is the weight of the last stage, or payload. This is the law of diminishing returns for space flight.

Obviously, the Soviet rocket experts found good use for the high thrust of their missiles. They had sufficient thrust so that they could afford to attempt lunar missions on an impressive scale. Their Lunik I shot of January 2, 1959, sent a final stage of 3,245 pounds hurtling toward the moon. Lunik's payload consisted of an 800-pound spherical package of instruments designed to measure solar radiation, cosmic rays and the magnetism of the moon. The Soviets did not announce in advance what mission the Lunik shot was designed to fulfill, so we do not know if it was supposed to go into orbit around the moon or to zoom off into space. In any event, Lunik I followed the latter course and entered interplanetary space where neither the earth's attraction nor that of the moon determined its trajectory. Instead, the sun's gravitational pull caught the wanderer and swept it into a solar orbit. Thus Lunik I became the first true space probe. Held in place by the same force that embraces the earth, Lunik I has become an artificial planet—the first on record—and it pursues an elliptical path around the sun. Its "year" is about 14 months. There is little chance that it will ever meet up with its parent planet. Lunik I has become a dead object in space, fated to whirl on its endless, unceasing course.

Lunik II scored a bull's-eye impact upon the moon's surface. To be sure, a rather spatial view of a bull's-eye, but a 150-mile circle of error was considered excellent marksmanship in 1959. More than marksmanship, it was exquisitely timed showmanship. Launched on September 12, 1959, Lunik II flashed across the earth-moon void in 35 hours. The moon rocket was apparently the same in thrust as the Lunik I shot. It carried a payload of 858 pounds which plunged toward the center of the moon's disk at a speed of 7,000 miles per hour and ejected a 58-pound spherical probe. The latter impacted upon the moon's surface at 2 minutes and 24 seconds after 5 P.M. (Eastern Daylight Time) on September 13—just 84 seconds later than Soviet scientists had predicted. At noon of September 15 Premier

Khrushchev arrived at Andrews Air Force Base to begin his tour of the United States. One of his first official acts was to present President Eisenhower with a memento—a replica of a pentagonal metal plate (Plate 8) which formed part of a volleyball-like sphere. Besides bearing the familiar hammer and sickle (superimposed upon a world grid) and the red star, ribbon wound around stalks of wheat bore the Communist slogan "Workers of the world, unite!" Radio Moscow announced that the first man-made object to reach the moon had been sterilized so as not to transfer any biological organisms to it.

The Soviet medallions ejected by Lunik II are buried deep in the moon's crust. Undoubtedly the more massive last stage, which hit the lunar surface shortly after the spherical probe, is splattered into many fragments. Some day lunar explorers may happen upon this historic earth-object but it seems quite improbable. The moon is already too thoroughly pocked with mile-wide craters—over 30,000 on the side we can see—to allow one much hope for digging up a tiny man-made meteorite. Studies on earth show that our planet is bombarded each day with many hundreds of tons of meteors, although only about a ton of the projectiles fall to earth. Only at rare intervals does a massive meteor crash through the earth's protective atmosphere and produce a visible crater. Visitors to Wilson, Arizona, can peer down into the famous Meteor Crater where a hole 4,000 feet wide and 500 feet deep testifies to a prehistoric impact of spectacular magnitude. It is interesting to note that the core of this deeply buried meteor has never been discovered.

On October 4, 1959, the second anniversary of Sputnik I, the Soviet rocket experts launched another impressive space vehicle. It was the third of a series to be sent on lunar missions. Again the last stage—some 3,423 pounds—streaked toward the moon, carrying a 614-pound space device, or "automatic interplanetary station," as the Russians called it. Lunik III was sent on a difficult and sensational assignment—object: to photograph the back side of the moon.

Since the moon circles the earth once a month and since its

period of rotation (its "day") is also one month, the moon keeps the same face turned to earth. The innermost planet of our solar system, Mercury, exhibits the same behavior toward our sun with the result that its bright side is intensely hot, i.e., about 700° F. at maximum. Our moon rotates with respect to the sun so it does not share Mercury's one-sided view of the sun.

A view of the hidden side of the moon could only be obtained if Lunik III interposed itself between the unseen face and the sun. On October 7 the Soviet space vehicle looped beyond the moon's orbit and proceeded to orient itself for picture-taking. The twin cameras were pointed at the moon by a combination of sun- and moon-sensors. First, the space device was oriented by an electronic device which sought out the sun (not a difficult target to seek in the blackness of space) and then a set of sensors sought out the moon's illuminated surface. Thus by a one-two operation the massive space camera was positioned to look at the moon; the actual propulsive power came from small reaction jets attached to the body of the space vehicle. Plate 9 illustrates the relative positions of Lunik III and the moon.

Lunik III circled beyond the moon's orbit and at a distance of some 40,000 miles from the moon the camera was kept pointing at the lunar surface. Two lenses, one 8 inches and the other 20 inches in focal length, focused the moon's image upon a single strip of 35-mm. film. Completely self-contained controls operated the camera for some 40 minutes. Then the film was automatically developed and dried. After processing the film was then televised back to earth—over 280,000 miles distant. This long-distance television was accomplished successfully.

The orbit of Lunik III, stretching 295,000 miles from earth, was calculated by digital (electronic) computers. The very complex mathematical analysis was begun in 1953 at the Mathematics Institute of the Academy of Sciences. Soviet scientists planned the orbit so that the moon's pull would change the motion of the space vehicle and cause it to pass over Soviet territory. This represented a very sophisticated astronautical flight program.

On October 18, after a two-week flight covering almost 800,-000 miles, Lunik III neared the earth. A radio command was given from a station in the Soviet Union and the 35-mm. film was again televised. The purpose of the encore was to transmit the pictures at closer range and thus achieve higher photographic quality in reproduction.

One of the first Soviet moon photographs is shown in Plate 10; presumably this is a retouched version of a close-range picture. Considering the complexity of the over-all photographic assignment, the detail shown of the far side of the moon is quite good. It can be estimated that had the same equipment orbited the earth at an altitude of 300 miles, it would have distinguished objects 200 feet in diameter. According to the time-honored custom of discoverers, the Soviets gave names to the prominent landmarks, calling them after scientific celebrities—usually of Soviet birth. For example, distinctive craters were named after (Mikhail) Lomonosov, (Konstantin) Tsiolkovsky and (Frédéric) Joliot-Curie. Lomonosov is regarded as the founder of much of Soviet science and Joliot-Curie, a Nobel Prize winner in chemistry, was a French scientist noted for his Communist ideology. Tsiolkovsky, whom we have mentioned as the father of Russian rocketry, suggested the use of liquid fuel for rockets as early as 1898. He also took very seriously the planning of a trip to the moon, so it was fitting that his name should grace a great lunar crater.

Soviet accomplishments on their lunar missions represent solid advances, even if they came as offshoots of objectives that were quite psycho-political in nature. They were so impressive to many people that the day of the manned lunar landing seemed close at hand early in the sixties. Yet for both the Soviet Union and the United States there remained a great technological gap to be bridged. A host of tough problems needed to be solved before man would set foot on the moon. These appeared so complex and perverse that the U.S. program for landing a man on the moon was officially placed in time as "beyond 1970." No Russian timetable for a lunar expedition has been revealed, but I believe that the Soviets' headstart in space, together with their high esteem for space triumphs, makes it probable that the first man on the moon will be a Russian. Were this feat to be accomplished late in 1967 it would mark the fiftieth anniversary of the famous October revolution in Russia.

Manned expeditions to the moon will be preceded by a long series of instrumented flights designed to test the performance of complex rockets and to transmit to earth data about the lunar surface. These lunar missions, begun in 1961, will involve increasingly large payloads and more versatile and sensitive equipment. Prior to the advent of very-high-thrust rockets, such as Saturn, the backbone of the U.S. lunar rocket program will be the Atlas-Agena-B and the Atlas-Centaur vehicles (Plate 11).

Atlas-Agena-B employs an Atlas ICBM as a booster and an Air Force second stage built by the Lockheed Aircraft Corporation. Agena-B uses IRFNA/UDMH as fuel, meaning a combination of red fuming nitric acid as oxidizer and hydrazine (technically, Unsymmetrical DiMethylHydrazine), which forms a high-performance fuel for space rockets. The Agena-B stage is five feet in diameter and is 25 feet long; it is powered by a 15,000-pound-thrust engine built by Bell Aircraft Company. A new feature of this second stage is that it contains its own guidance system and is "restartable" in space. The Atlas-Agena-B combination is capable of launching a 5,000-pound satellite into a 300-mile earth orbit or of projecting an 800-pound payload on deep-space missions. NASA plans call for the use of 16 Atlas-Agena-B rockets.

The 800-pound spacecraft, used for lunar reconnaissance missions in the early sixties, incorporates a 300-pound instrument package which unfolds to form the lunar impact device shown in Plate 12. The experiments are the brain child of the Jet Propulsion Laboratory at the California Institute of Technology and come under the heading of Project Ranger. The instrumented package for the Ranger spacecraft are constructed by the Aeronutronics Division of Ford Motor Company. After launching by the Atlas-Agena-B rocket, the 12-foot-long space-craft is guided toward its target, the moon, and after a flight of almost three days it will arrive in the vicinity of the moon.

When the Ranger spacecraft nears the moon, a television camera will take close-up pictures of the lunar surface and transmit them to earth; it is expected that objects ten feet in diameter will be recognizable. Then, as the vehicle approaches to about 25 miles of the surface, the instrument package will be detached and slowed down to 300 mph by a retrorocket. The spacecraft itself will crash into the moon at a speed of 5,500 mph. An impact at 300 mph is known in space circles as a "rough" or "crash" landing, but equipment can be built to survive such a pummeling. In fact, design specifications call for survival up to 1,000 g. A variety of techniques serve as shock absorbers. For example, crushable honeycomb structures serve to protect equipment nested inside. In this way a small, rugged seismometer can be landed on the moon and used to record lunar seisms, or moonquakes. Sufficient radio power is supplied to transmit seismic data for a period of a month. Such data are extremely useful to scientists seeking to analyze the inner structure of the moon.

The development of the Centaur provides the United States with greater payload capability than that offered by the Atlas-Agena-B. Centaur is the name for the second stage fitted to the Atlas, but it is also used to apply to the entire rocket. The Centaur engine delivers 15,000 pounds of thrust and burns liquid hydrogen and oxygen. This mixture provides about one third more thrust than kerosene-oxygen systems. Liquid hydrogen is supercold, being minus 423° F., and burns to produce a 5,500° F. temperature in the combustion chamber. Unlike the Agena-B stage, which appears to be tacked on to the Atlas booster as a make-fit, the Centaur stage fits smoothly, forming a sleek rocket. Its twin engines in the second stage can propel an 8,500-pound satellite into a low earth orbit or send a three-quarter-ton payload to the moon. The high-power second stage makes possible higher velocities than Agena-B can impart to payloads and thus Centaur opens the road to well-instrumented missions to other planets.

Centaur missions include massive "orbiters," or space vehicles sent into orbit around the moon. Using proper guidance and retrothrust to "kill off" undesired speed, a spacecraft can be made to become an artificial satellite of the moon just as Sputnik I orbited the earth. Aside from purely scientific measurements of radiation and magnetism, such orbiters can provide a survey of the lunar surface.

The high payloads projectible with Centaur make possible true "soft" landings on the moon. For such landings the descending spacecraft needs not only sufficient rocket thrust to offset its downward speed, but it must carry along the sensors, computers and mechanisms for guiding the instrument package to a gentle, vertical descent. The moon, of course, lacks significant atmosphere to allow for air-braking; rocket thrust is the only means available to "kill off" the speed of the incoming vehicle. Radar altimeters aboard the spacecraft, together with radio guidance devices, feed their information on the craft's descent into electronic computers and these, in turn, instruct the rocket engine so that more or less thrust is generated. In addition, the retrorocket needs to be directed so that the craft comes down on a vertical course and does not slam into a crater wall or mountain ridge.

Given the opportunity to have instruments soft-landed on the moon, scientists have a wide choice of possible experiments. They are interested in learning about the traces of gas that may remain on the moon. Even more interesting is an analysis of the moon's crust and close-up, even magnified, views of the lunar environment. An ingenious experiment, using both techniques of X-ray analysis and nuclear physics, will permit scientists to determine what elements exist in the lunar soil and rock. The data, obtained by automatic functioning of the analytical devices, will be telemetered back to earth.

Routine measurements of lunar temperatures, cosmic-ray activity, and solar X-rays will be made from stationary "instrument bases" on the moon. Research is being promoted to develop a microscope for the examination of moon soil samples. A sticky tape or some other device will be used to transport samples for examination and a self-focusing microscope will project images which are then transmitted to earth stations. Such microscopic studies will give detailed information about the nature of the lunar crust prior to the time when samples can be scooped from the moon's surface and returned to earth.

Scientists are striving to perfect marvelously ingenious devices to gain information about the moon before man's arrival on the scene. By 1965 they will have a much better understanding of the lunar environment, all made possible by relatively small packages of instruments landed in fixed locations upon the moon. Up to this time the lunar surveys will depend upon the Atlas booster as the first stage in the launching of spacecraft. This imposes a severe restriction upon payloads, even though Centaur eases this somewhat, and it is necessary to go to a new class of boosters to accommodate heavier payloads and higher stages which will make return flights possible. Here we are dealing with booster thrust in excess of one million pounds and ultimately even above ten million pounds. Such are the thrusts Saturn and Nova engines will provide after 1965 and 1970, respectively.

We do not need to wait for round-trip missions, first with small packages of instruments and later with men, to tell us that the moon is no oasis for space travelers. During its two-week-long day, the bright surface of the moon roasts under a searing hot sun and surfaces at the Equator soar to temperatures above the boiling point of water. And during the long lunar night, the surface cools off very rapidly, since there is no insulating layer of atmosphere, and the temperature drops to minus 240° F. This range of temperature, cycling over a 500-degree variation, is twice that of the greatest extremes ever recorded on earth.

Scientists have speculated that there might be some water trapped in the lunar crust, but this remains to be ascertained.

Man's most necessary element, oxygen, is absent in the form of a free gas but there is hope that oxygen might be made available by processing lunar minerals. This implies a sophisticated moon mission, and, in effect, a lunar base with men and equipment capable of "mining" oxygen. The first men on the moon will have to carry all their life-support system with them.

The lack of atmosphere exposes a lunar visitor to the direct rays of the sun—to intense ultraviolet radiation and to some solar X-rays. Lunar explorers will have to be shielded against this harmful radiation and it may even be necessary for them to take cover during times of unusual solar and cosmic-ray activity. However, permanently recording instruments at lunar stations will provide the essential data about these hazards long before man sets foot on lunar soil.

It is because of the moon's inhospitable climate that a large number of instrumented missions are required to scout out the strange territory and report back on lunar conditions. For example, mobile instruments, discussed in the following chapter, will provide data on the firmness of the surface so that an exploratory mission would not vanish in a sea of dust. Once the lay of the land is foreseen, then beacons can be emplaced on the moon to guide future missions to a safe landing.

The world will await most anxiously the landing of men upon the moon, but in a sense this will probably come as something of an anticlimax to scientists and perhaps even to laymen. The moon will not be a stranger to us when manned missions arrive, for the many lunar surveys—from orbiters, from fixed lunar probes and from roving lunar vehicles—will probe the secrets of the uninhabited satellite. The question of life on the moon will probably be settled before man arrives there. Scientists do not have much doubt on this score, because, as Professor Harold Urey explained:

Life would not be supported on the surface of the Moon in any important way. It would be very difficult to be sure that terrestrial organisms would not find some way to support themselves at least temporarily in the subsurface regions of the Moon where there may be carbon compounds of an inorganic type, that is, produced by inorganic processes. It is very doubtful if there is any indigenous life on the Moon—so doubtful, in fact, that it can be considered as a certainty within the usual definition of that term.

Professor Urey raises the issue of possible contamination of the moon by organisms that might be carried there aboard lunar probes. The problem has worried some scientists so much that they formed a committee called CETEX to "consider the implications of contamination of the moon and the planets by extraterrestrial exploration." The group urged that certain types of contamination should be guarded against. Scientists have urged that all space vehicles bent on lunary or interplanetary missions should be sterilized before take-off. The reason for the scientific alarm is explained in the case of the moon by Dr. Joshua Lederberg of the University of Wisconsin and Dr. Dean B. Cowie of the Carnegie Institution of Washington in an article titled "Moondust," which appeared in *Science* magazine:

Astronomers suppose that the moon is covered by a layer of dust of great antiquity. This dust is cosmic material captured by the moon gravitational field and presumably left undisturbed by atmospheric and biological alteration. It should therefore contain a continuing record of cosmic history as informative with respect to the biochemical origins of life as the fossil-bearing sediments of the earth's crust have been in the study of its later evolution.

A pinch of moondust, untouched by anything from earth which might disturb the record, would be an "astronomical Rosetta stone" bearing a partial biography of the solar system and perhaps of the first phases of life. These may be no more than faint clues—elemental combinations of molecules representing nature's first dice throws in the building up of complex assemblies of atoms. Analysis of moondust, providing it is not contaminated by the hand of man, may shed light on the old theory that hydrocarbons have drifted through cosmic space.

This panspermia hypothesis has been rejuvenated recently because of new ideas about the origin of the planets.

To the layman, the exploration of the moon will be a thrilling venture into a strange land, a vista of mountains, dusty plains, rocky craters and deep fissures. And perhaps most intoxicating of all will be the new view of the earth against a panoply of brilliant stars, presided over by the spectacle of the naked sun with its colorful, changing corona and dazzling eruptions of flaming gas.

To the scientist, the deep fascination and treasured value of the moon lies in the fundamental knowledge, largely derived from a microscopic and chemical analysis of the lunar crust.

The spirit of adventure and the quest for knowledge both beckon man on to the moon. It is a commentary upon the nature of man that his haste to reach the moon—his spending of billions of dollars to fashion enormously powerful rockets— is motivated primarily by a bitterly fought contest between two earth powers, both seeking technological supremacy and, with it, first rank among the other nations.

7

SATURN AND NOVA

THE APPROACH to the moon, begun in the early sixties by a score of reconnaissance spacecraft carrying small instrumented payloads, moves into its second phase in the mid-sixties with the development of Saturn—America's entry in the heavyweight class of space vehicles. But even mighty Saturn with its million and a half pounds of thrust will not permit sending man to the moon on round-trip missions. For this, a new propulsion plant—the Nova engine—is being developed.

Reliability has become a key word to space engineers. For this reason NASA chose to use a medium-thrust, reliable rocket engine for its massive Saturn booster. High total thrust is attained by ganging together or clustering eight medium-thrust engines to produce 1.5 million pounds of thrust. Actually, NASA's decision to bank upon the cluster approach amounted to a confirmation of a decision made earlier by the U.S. Army.

Little is to be gained by reciting the early history of Project

Saturn. It is sufficient to relate that the Defense Department authorized the Army to undertake development of high-thrust engines at its Huntsville, Alabama, facility. Dr. von Braun, as technical director of the Development Operations Division of the Army Ballistic Missile Agency, selected the Jupiter engine for clustering in the first stage of the mammoth rocket. Since Saturn is the outlying neighbor of Jupiter in the solar system, it was a natural name for the big rocket. After giving von Braun a go-ahead on Saturn, the Defense Department seems to have second thoughts about the need for a large rocket of the Saturn type. It agreed to transfer the entire project, including ten laboratory facilities at Huntsville and all personnel, to NASA. President Eisenhower then named this facility the George C. Marshall Space Flight Center, in honor of America's soldier-statesman.

The Jupiter engine had a good reputation as a reliable rocket power plant. It was a Jupiter-C that shot America's first satellite into orbit. Moreover, the propulsion plant performed faithfully in many tests of the Army's intermediate-range ballistic missile as well as in space shots where it was used as a first stage. The rocket engine designed for the Saturn's first stage is an improved Jupiter design known as the Rocketdyne H-1 engine. Manufactured by the North American Aviation Company, the H-1 engine has a thrust capacity of 188,000 pounds. It burns RP-1, a kerosene-like jet fuel, and liquid oxygen. A photograph of the H-1 engine is shown in Plate 13, along with fuel tanks for the first stage, which is called S-I.

The Saturn booster of S-I stage is designed to be the basic work horse of the heavy-payload flight missions from 1965-70. It is to be used in a three-stage, or C-1, configuration and later this will be transformed to a C-2 version having a new, high-thrust second stage. A still more powerful and complex version, the C-3, may be produced at a much later date. The drawing in Fig. 8 illustrates the C-1 and C-2 versions, alongside a Centaur.

Because of the reliability factor, Saturn vehicles embody the principle of using upper stages from other space vehicles. Thus the Centaur upper stage becomes the upper stage of C-1 and C-2. By the same token the second stage of C-1 becomes the third stage of C-2. The advantage of this hand-me-over system is that the new vehicle has a greater chance of success since fewer un-tried component stages are employed.

Naturally, each new stage such as the S-I or basic Saturn

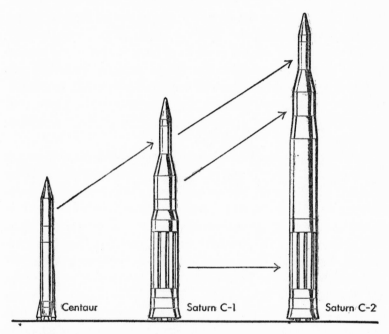

Fig. 8. Drawing showing relative size of Saturn and Centaur and inter-changeability of upper stages. *NASA*

booster is tested exhaustively on the ground before it is com-mitted to a flight. For this purpose a 177-foot static test tower is used to position and restrain the rocket stage while the engines are tested. Directly below the engines is a water-cooled deflecting shield and tunnel through which the exhaust flame is channeled.

The pattern of development for the C-1 Saturn vehicle is as follows: launch of S-I stage plus dummy upper stages (1961);

launch of vehicle with dummy upper stage (1962-3); check-out of all three stages (1963); and first operational flight (1964). A total of ten test firings will be required to prove out the performance of each intermediate vehicle so that reliance can be placed upon space vehicles designed to carry real payloads.

Some concept of the engineering task faced in developing the Saturn may be gained by considering the first stage, or S-I. As shown in Plate 13 the fuel tanks for this stage consist of a central 105-inch-diameter tank and a cluster of eight 70-inch-diameter tanks. These carry 375 tons of propellant along with the essential oxygen. Because of the high rate of fuel consumption, both liquids have to be pumped from the cylindrical tanks at high speed. This task in itself requires powerful turbopumps for which the power requirements are considerable. The complexity of the plumbing shown in the H-1 engine attests to the problems encountered in harnessing the energy of kerosene mixed with oxygen. There is always a chance that a single engine will fail, but Saturn is designed to take off under such a contingency.

The second stage of the C-1 Saturn is called S-IV and it uses four improved Centaur engines. Each of the new engines is rated at 17,500 pounds of thrust, so that the S-IV stage produces a total of 70,000 pounds of thrust. Improvements in design may raise the individual ratings to more than 20,000 pounds of thrust. As mentioned in describing the Centaur engine earlier, it burns liquid hydrogen and oxygen and provides considerably more thrust than kerosene and oxygen. Rocket men use a performance rating for various combinations of fuels and oxidizers which assigns a value of 290 to kerosene and liquid oxygen. On this scale, liquid hydrogen and oxygen rates close to 400. The difference in fuel ratings might not seem sensational but the nature of rocketry is such that substitution of liquid hydrogen nearly doubles the payload that can be propelled upward.

Liquid hydrogen poses many problems as a rocket fuel. It is more difficult to store than kerosene and its supercold makes pumping more complex than for an ordinary liquid. There are highly technical problems such as "cavitation," bubble formation which interferes with the pumping. However, the advantage of superior thrust is so great that liquid hydrogen is a premium fuel. It may someday be replaced by an even more potent chemical, fluorine, but fluorine is such a corrosive material that it will have to undergo a long development. Liquid-hydrogen engines are theoretically capable of being upgraded to much higher ratings than the 20,000-pound-thrust design of the Centaur power plant. However, NASA experts felt it was too risky a proposition to jump to more powerful engines using the new fuel, and consequently the S-IV stage is geared to the Centaur-class engines.

The combination of S-I and S-IV, in other words a two-stage Saturn, can put a five-ton satellite into a low earth orbit. This two-stage Saturn is a massive package involving a number of transportation bottlenecks. For example, the S-IV stage is being built by the Douglas Aircraft Corporation at its Santa Monica, California, plant. It is 18 feet in diameter and for shipping purposes is 50 feet in length. Such a package is far too big for shipment by rail or truck, so it is shipped by boat via the Panama Canal to the Gulf of Mexico, where it is transferred by barge. Then it proceeds by a roundabout route to Huntsville, Alabama, or rather to the Redstone Arsenal which fronts Wheeler Lake. At the Marshall Space Flight Center the two stages are mated and checked; then they go by barge to Cape Canaveral.

A special launch area has been established for Saturn tests and space missions. It lies due east of the Cocoa-Titusville airport and is located at the far end of the Atlantic Missile Range, north of the eight launch pads reserved for ICBM's. Two launch areas, Saturn I and II, are built on the thin, sandy stretch that separates the Atlantic Ocean from the Banana River. About a mile from the launch pad, the various stages of the Saturn are brought together in a staging building which is almost large enough to shelter a football field. Here final tests are given to the structure preparatory to moving the Saturn vehicle to its launch pad.

The third stage—and last for the C-1 Saturn—is called S-V. It is a slightly modified version of the Centaur and has a thrust rating in the 35-to-40,000-pound class. Built by Convair Astronautics at San Diego, the S-V stage has the coast-and-restart feature, plus a self-contained guidance system controlling all three stages. Thus the last stage, plus payload, can be given a final touch of speed or a nudge in the right direction by command from within the vehicle.

The final C-1 version of Saturn, comprising three stages, is officially estimated to cost $20 million, including development charges. Rocket costs are usually quite approximate and this estimate may be regarded as a rosy one. The 185-foot rocket, about twice the length of ICBM's, is capable of lifting heavy payloads on low-velocity, i.e., near-earth missions. For example, the C-1 Saturn can place a 20,000-pound satellite in a low earth orbit. Using the rosy estimate of Saturn costs, this amounts to $1,000 per pound of payload.

If the C-1 Saturn is used for deep-space missions, then the payload drops. The payload sent to escape velocity as a space probe is about 6,000 pounds. A lunar soft landing, involving retrothrust on board the last stage, cuts this payload to one fourth, i.e., to about 1,500 pounds. On this basis, a pound of payload soft-landed on the moon would cost about $15,000. Thus, if space scientists are at all cost-conscious, they should be deeply concerned with cutting down on the weight of lunar equipment.

Soft-landing of equipment on the moon's surface has been described in the previous chapter. We detailed a number of experiments to be performed with soft-landed equipment. The roving vehicle is one of the most ambitious projects for Saturn vehicles. Plate 14 shown an artist's conception of such a mission after landing on the moon. Retrothrust, properly applied, lowers the spacecraft to the lunar surface; then four radar reflectors serve to orient the descending vehicle horizontally. The

PLATE 1. Replica of Sputnik III. The device is shown on display in the Science Pavilion of the U.S.S.R. Industrial Exhibition in Moscow.

NASA

PLATE 2. Photograph of a paddle-wheel, solar-powered satellite.

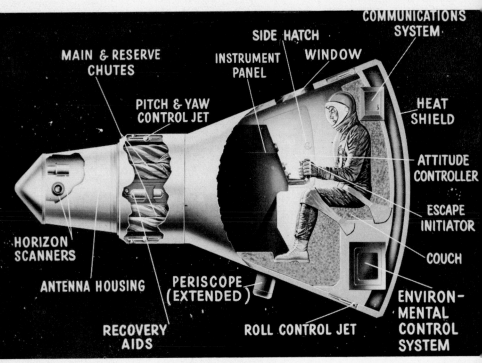

COMMUNICATIONS SYSTEM

SIDE HATCH

INSTRUMENT PANEL

WINDOW

MAIN & RESERVE CHUTES

HEAT SHIELD

PITCH & YAW CONTROL JET

ATTITUDE CONTROLLER

ESCAPE INITIATOR

HORIZON SCANNERS

COUCH

ANTENNA HOUSING

PERISCOPE (EXTENDED)

ENVIRON-MENTAL CONTROL SYSTEM

RECOVERY AIDS

ROLL CONTROL JET

NASA

PLATE 3. Cutaway view of the Mercury capsule.

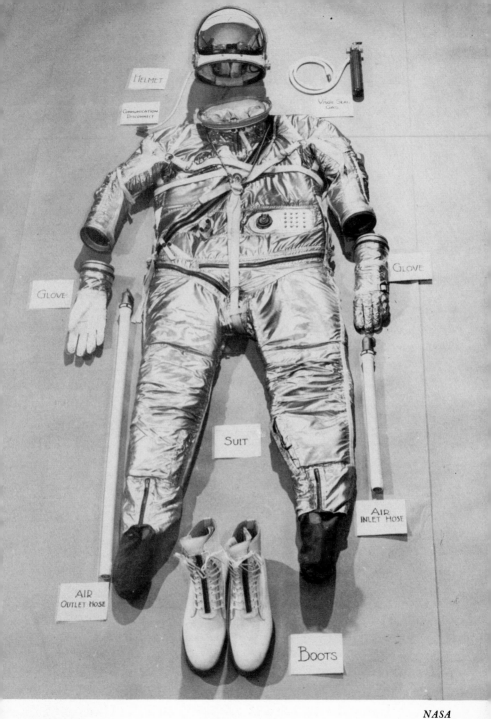

HELMET

COMMUNICATION DISCONNECT

VISOR SEAL GAS

GLOVE

GLOVE

SUIT

AIR INLET HOSE

AIR OUTLET HOSE

BOOTS

PLATE 4. Layout showing the various parts of the space suit worn by Mercury astronauts.

PLATE 5. Mercury astronaut is shown with "boiler plate" version of the space capsule.

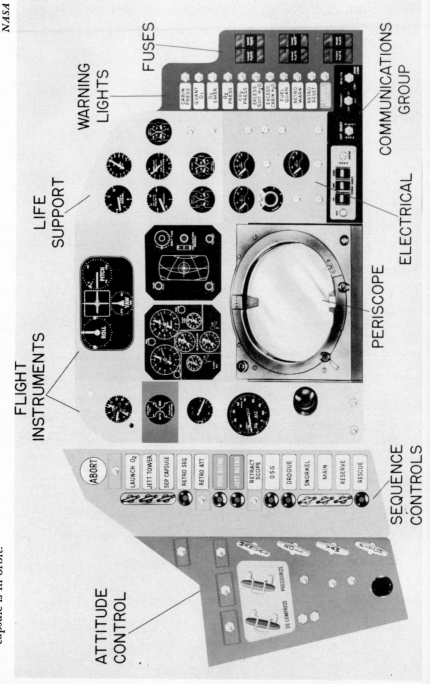

PLATE 6. Mercury capsule's instrument panel. The periscope provides the astronaut with a view of the earth when the capsule is in orbit.

NASA

FUSES

WARNING LIGHTS

CABIN PRESS
QUANT O₂
O₂ EMER
O₂ PRESS
CO₂ PRESS
EXCESS SUIT H₂O
EXCESS CABIN H₂O
FUEL QUAN
RETRO WARN
RETRO RESET

COMMUNICATIONS GROUP

LIFE SUPPORT

ELECTRICAL

FLIGHT INSTRUMENTS

PITCH
YAW
ROLL

PERISCOPE

SEQUENCE CONTROLS

ABORT
LAUNCH O₂
JETT TOWER
SEP CAPSULE
RETRO SEQ
RETRO ATT
FIRE RETRO
JETT RETRO
RETRACT SCOPE
.05G
DROGUE
SNORKEL
MAIN
RESERVE
RESCUE

ATTITUDE CONTROL

PITCH
ROLL
YAW
AUX

PRESSURIZE
DE-COMPRESS

PLATE 7. View of the Atlas missile mated to the Mercury capsule.

Courtesy Soviet Embassy,
Washington, D.C.

PLATE 8. The first man-made object to hit the moon. This volley-ball-sized sphere composed of metallic pentagons struck the moon on September 13, 1959 at 5:02 P.M. Eastern Daylight Time.

Courtesy Soviet Embassy,
Washington, D.C.

PLATE 9. Sketch showing Lunik III (automatic interplanetary station) photographing the moon. Arrows at the left indicate the direction of the sun's rays. Banks of solar cells provide electrical power for the device.

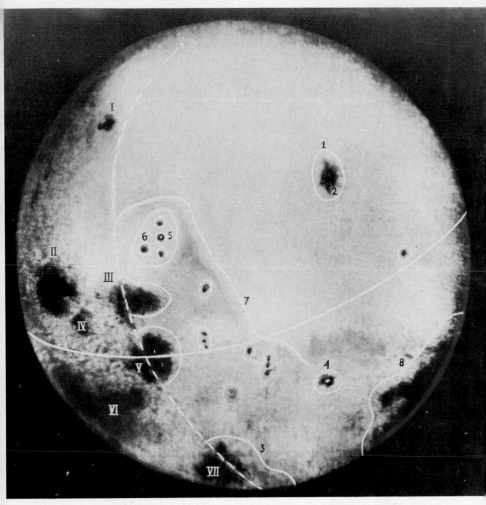

Courtesy Soviet Embassy, Washington, D. C.

PLATE 10. Photograph of the far side of the moon, taken by a camera aboard Lunik III. Numbers identify the following physical features: 1. Sea of Moscow (180 miles in diameter); 2. Gulf of Astronauts; 3. Continuation of Mare Australe; 4. Tsiolkovsky crater; 5. Lomonosov crater; 6. Joliot-Curie crater; 7. Sovietsky Mountain Range; 8. Sea of Dreams. The continuous white line across the moon is the equator. The broken line indicates the edge visible from Earth. To the left are well-known mare such as I. Humboldt; II. Crisium; III. Maginis; IV. Sea of Waves; V. Smythii; VI. Foecunditatis; VII. Mare Australe.

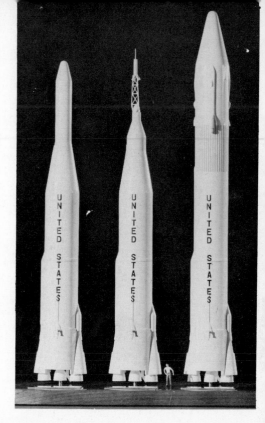

PLATE 11. Atlas missiles with three different upper stages. A. Agena-B; B. Mercury capsule with escape tower; C. Centaur.

PLATE 12. A Ranger spacecraft nears the moon. Television close-ups of the lunar surface are transmitted back to Earth. The core of the instrument package "roughlands" on the moon and keeps transmitting radio data.

PLATE 13. The Rocketdyne H-1 engine. Eight of these will be used in the first stage of the Saturn vehicle. Fuel tanks for the first stage are shown in the background.

PLATE 14. Roving vehicle trundles off its landing pad after soft impact upon the moon.

NASA

PLATE 15. An Atlas carrying a dummy Mercury capsule lifts off the launch pad at Cape Canaveral. Note the vernier jet.

PLATE 16. Manned Orbital Laboratory. Insert shows the last stage fitted to the launch vehicle.

NASA

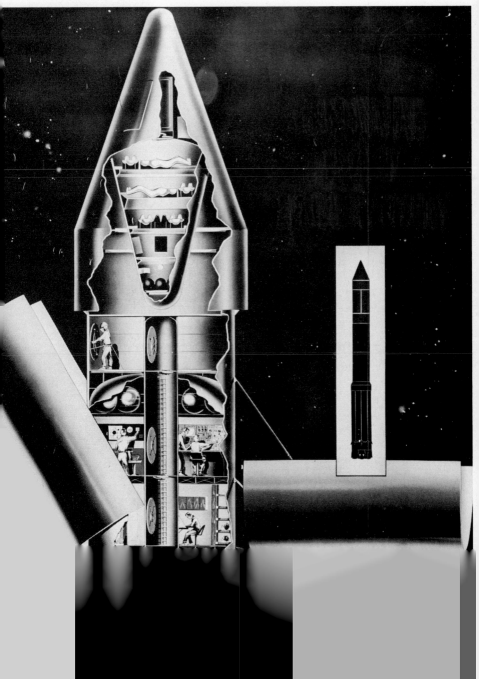

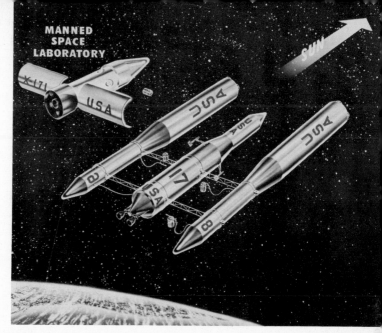

PLATE 17. Sketch of a lunar-bound vehicle (17) being refueled in orbit prior to beginning its journey to the moon. A manned space laboratory orbits alongside with a space crew to service the huge spacecraft.

PLATE 18. Close-up view of the Nova engine designed to produce 1.5 million pounds of thrust.

PLATE 19. Launching.

PLATE 20. Second stage firing.

LUNAR

RETURN

MISSION

Plates 19-25

PLATE 21. Third stage firing.

PLATE 22. Fourth stage rotation.

PLATE 23. Spacemen emerge from their mooncraft and prepare to explore the terrain.

PLATE 24. Take-off from Moon with fifth stage.

PLATE 25. The re-entry vehicle approaches the earth as it nears the completion of its lunar mission.

PLATE 26. Sketch showing the Nimbus weather satellite surveying the Earth's cloud cover. Two paddle wheels provide solar power for the orbital weather station.

NASA

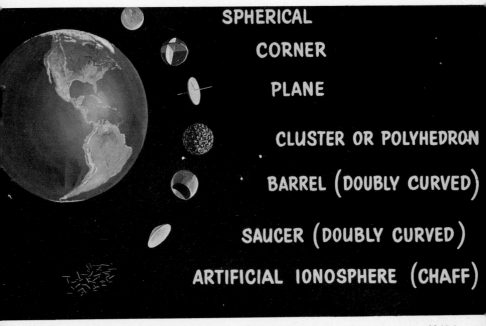

SPHERICAL

CORNER

PLANE

CLUSTER OR POLYHEDRON

BARREL (DOUBLY CURVED)

SAUCER (DOUBLY CURVED)

ARTIFICIAL IONOSPHERE (CHAFF)

PLATE 27. Various reflectors for radio communication.

PLATE 28. A double-header satellite. On top is the Naval Research Laboratory satellite designed to measure solar radiation. It was launched "piggyback" on top of Transit IIA, the Navy's orbital "lighthouse" satellite. The two satellites were separated by a spring release, but traveled in very similar orbits.

PLATE 29. The U.S. Air Force Discoverer satellite. The vehicle is 19 feet in length and 5 feet in diameter.

PLATE 30. Photo of Midas II. This is the second stage of a vehicle designed to give early warning of ICBM attack. Infrared sensors pointed towards the Earth detect heat emanating from the exhaust of ICBMs during launch.

PLATE 31. The world's largest radio telescope (1962). Built by the U.S. Navy at
Sugar Grove, West Virginia. The "Big Dish" measures 600 feet from rim to rim
and weighs 20,000 tons. It can be aimed in any direction by swinging the cradle
and by energizing the motors on the circular base drive.

amount of retrothrust applied must be carefully metered so that the downward velocity is "killed off" as the vehicle reaches the lunar surface and not before. Rockets can supply only limited hovering time, and too early a retrothrust would bring the vehicle to a halt high above the lunar surface, leaving it to plunge down thereafter. To take up any undue impact, grasshopper-leg structures act as shock absorbers. The lunar rover is then automatically assembled, meaning unfolded and inflated, and it is commanded by remote control from earth posts to make excursions over the moon's surface. Power for propelling the mobile lunar station is supplied from within the structure. Solar cells are used to recharge the vehicle's batteries.

The C-2 version of Saturn requires only one new stage, the second; all others are carry-overs from C-1. This new second stage uses high-energy propellants, namely the liquid hydrogen-oxygen combination, and a tenfold more powerful rocket engine than that employed in Centaur. This means that the new rocket engine for this S-II stage will generate 200,000 pounds of thrust or slightly more than the H-1 motor which burns conventional fuel. It is not the power rating of the engine that is so significant; it is the fact that it is used in a second stage and that it uses a high-energy propellant. Because of the technical thorns embedded in the technology of liquid hydrogen, the S-II engine will require considerable development. Four such engines will power the S-II stage, producing a total thrust of 800,000 pounds or about half that unleashed in the first stage. As a result the weight-lifting ability of the C-2 Saturn will be impressive.

A 25-ton permanent earth-orbital laboratory can be blasted into space by use of the C-2 rocket. Plate 16 illustrates how such a manned space laboratory might look. The vehicle is a shell-shaped object some 18 feet in diameter; its cylindrical sides open and unfold to collect solar energy as a supplemental power source. During take-off, the space crew would occupy form-fitting couches near the tip of the spacecraft, but once in orbit they would descend through a central tube and occupy pressurized quarters.

One important use for such a huge orbital station would be the servicing of outward-bound spacecraft, particularly those bent on manned lunar missions. Neither the C-1 nor the C-2 Saturn has the power to accomplish such a mission on a round-trip basis. But there exists the alternative of using an orbital service station to refuel a Saturn (minus its booster stage, or coupled to another stage hooked on in orbit). Such an orbital refueling operation requires not only fuel tankers in orbit but also a crew of men to service the spaceship. An artist's conception of this orbital rendezvous is shown in Plate 17. Astronauts leave their mother ship through special air locks and, equipped with spacesuits and small compressed gas jets, they maneuver to the spacecraft to check its condition and to refuel it with propellants pumped from the tanker.

An orbitally refueled Saturn might be used for a round-trip lunar mission, taking a three-man crew to a soft landing on the moon. Such a flight would not, however, mark man's first close visit to the moon. A circumlunar manned flight is very much easier in terms of space propulsion than a soft landing and return to earth. The reason for this is obvious by now: Two additional flight stages are required to land and take off from the moon. NASA's Project Apollo contemplates using a Saturn vehicle to take a three-man crew around the moon and back to earth. Such a flight, probable later in the sixties, will take man on an extended cruise through space lasting about two weeks. It will be preceded by test cruises of the Saturn vehicle in near-earth space in order to prove out the rocket and to test out the return-to-earth re-entry of the last stage.

Re-entry of a space vehicle presents some problems different from those of the return from earth orbit of the Mercury capsule type. For one thing, the lunar vehicle is much more massive and it does not re-enter from an orbital, circular path. It could be kicked into an orbital pattern by use of additional rocket thrust properly directed but this complicates design and increases the weight of the last stage. A vehicle returning from a lunar mission and attempting to land on earth must come in along a certain flight pattern or "re-entry corridor." The "neck" of this corridor is rather narrow, being about seven miles wide, so that the spaceship needs to be guided with the utmost precision. If it comes in too high, it will overshoot the earth and swing out into space; if it dives too low it will porpoise too steeply into the atmosphere and kill the crew.

The towering 230-foot-high Saturn C-2 is not the ultimate in missile design. A C-3 design contemplates adding one more stage, making five in all, to give a total thrust of 1.3 million pounds in the upper stages, plus the 1.5 million in the booster. This mammoth Saturn, due in the late 1960's, will be especially useful for deep-space missions although not of the manned type. One or two stages of this rocket ship may be nuclear powered, provided nuclear rocket engines prove reliable for space propulsion.

Saturn stretches, but by no means exhausts, the potential of ordinary or chemical propellants for powering rockets. North American Aviation has a NASA contract for the development of a vastly improved chemically fueled power plant. Built at the Rocketdyne Division's facility in Los Angeles, the new rocket engine is known as the F-1, or Nova, engine. Nova is the term for "new star" and technically it means a star which suddenly flares up with fantastic brilliance. Such novae, or exploding stars, are not unusual for the astronomer to view with a high-power telescope, but they rarely occur so as to be visible to the naked eye. Such records as are known show that only one super exploding star is observed every several centuries.

The Nova engine is designed to burn jet fuel and liquid oxygen to produce a thrust of 1.5 million pounds. In other words, one Nova F-1 engine equals eight Saturn H-1 motors. Yet, like the Saturn engine, the new Nova motor is designed to be clustered in the first stage of a gigantic booster designed for sending manned missions to the moon and to the planets. Such missions, employing a six-engine booster and appropriate upper stages, will be capable of lunar landings and return without necessity for orbital rendezvous and refueling.

Plate 18 illustrates the huge size of the Nova power plant. The over-all length of the engine is 20 feet and it has a nozzle diameter of 12 feet. Operating at full capacity, the engine gulps propellants at the rate of almost three tons per second. The turbopump required to deliver the propellants at this rate consumes 55,000 horsepower, which is supplied by a separate gas generator. Rocket designers expect that it will be 1967 before the F-1 engine is perfected. They need to acquire fundamental experience with the behavior of combustion processes where such a flood of fuel and oxygen gushes into the combustion chamber. The object, as in any propulsion plant designed for rockets, is to provide a constant flow of superhot exhaust gas, discharged in a steady stream unmarked by violent fluctuations. Many hours of static tests will be required to work out the proper design for the engine so that it will withstand the high stress of temperature and pressure within the combustion chamber. The engine, tested at Edwards Air Force Base in California, produces a deafening roar next to which the noise of a jet plane seems mild.

Various designs have been made for Nova boosters with four, six and eight engines clustered together. A total thrust in the range of six to 12 million pounds is involved. The height of the spacecraft is no greater than that of Saturn C-2, but it is designed to be much fatter, measuring 44 feet in diameter at the base. With a launch thrust of eight million pounds, a payload of about 140 tons could be placed in a low earth orbit. Approximately 35 tons could be shot to the moon. Such is the respective capability for the two- and three-stage Nova-class vehicles.

When we come to consider a five-stage Nova-type vehicle, such as would be capable of round-trip manned lunar missions, the payload returnable to earth shrinks in size. As Dr. Lee A. DuBridge summed it up: "One might almost put it down as a rule about space—namely, it is expensive to get there and even more expensive to get back." Estimates on the payload returnable to earth depend upon the nature of the propellants used in the upper stages and the kind of re-entry. Using high-energy propellants and high-speed re-entry, it appears that a six-ton lunar craft could be brought back to earth.

A five-stage lunar return mission, using Nova power plants, is shown in the accompanying series of sketches. Plate 19 depicts the launching at Cape Canaveral with the huge service structure withdrawn to avoid blast damage from the take-off. The next illustration shows the moon rocket heading upward with the big booster rocket parachuting back to earth. The idea in recovering the first stage is to cut costs and reuse the booster for another flight. The firing of the third-stage engines takes place after the second stage has been shed and the rocket is on its way to the moon.

Plate 22 shows the fourth stage being guided to the moon, ready for ignition of the retrothrust jet to kill off its velocity and then offset the downward pull of the moon. The next sketch (Plate 23) shows the moonship resting on its spiderlike mounts on the lunar surface. Two hardy astronauts, the first men on the moon, climb out of the craft to survey the new environment. A companion mooncraft in the background serves as a back-up vehicle in case of accident to the other ship.

To return to earth, the astronauts ignite the single engine of the fifth stage and head for home. The escape velocity from the moon is only 5,325 miles per hour, in contrast to the corresponding figure of 25,050 mph for the earth, so the fifth-stage motor does not have to be extremely powerful to propel the remaining weight of the vehicle away from the moon. The last sketch illustrates the approach of the manned capsule, minus its discarded motor, to the earth's surface. Finally, the capsule descends to a designated landing area by means of atmospheric braking and by parachuting.

Saturn and Nova represent man's attempts to harness chemical energy to project massive vehicles into space. Saturn is designed to bear the burden of space missions from 1965-70. Nova's time scale is less certain, owing to the fact that many problems have to be solved before Nova engines can be trusted for manned space missions. Official estimates by NASA put this day beyond 1970. Success with Nova motors will pave the way for space exploration beyond the moon on missions taking more than a few weeks. The requirements for such flights demand even larger payloads, and if reliance is placed upon chemical fuels, this inevitably means even more massive spacecraft.

Nuclear engines, burning compact, energy-rich uranium, are obvious candidates for the propulsion of spacecraft on long missions. Interplanetary travel taxes chemically powered craft to the limit and nuclear power seems the logical next choice for rocket engines. In addition, deep-ranging spacecraft will have large internal power requirements for communications equipment, and nuclear power clearly can supply this need.

Some atomic enthusiasts have tried to play down the role of chemical energy in space propulsion, even to the extent of saying that lunar rockets would have to be nuclear powered. Such is not the case; engines burning liquid oxygen and jet fuel or hydrogen can do the job and have every promise of success, while nuclear rockets are still in the cocoon stage. There can be little doubt, however, that the nuclear rocket promises to become a superior propulsive device in the more distant future.

8

PEACEFUL USES OF SATELLITES

LUNAR spaceships and huge booster rockets are still in the future. Before proceeding to problems of interplanetary travel, let us consider the peacetime and military applications for earth satellites.

The earth's population of artificial moons is growing rapidly. Many of the orbital devices shot into near-earth space have paths which will keep them in orbit for many decades and even centuries. Given the relatively short life of most electronic gadgets, the satellites in orbit pass quickly from the "active" to "dead" category. By "active" we mean they contain power sources and emit signals. We use the word "dead" to describe an orbital device which no longer serves its intended purpose.

One can classify a satellite according to its purpose, as, for example, a meteorological or a geodetic device. But with advances in instrumentation and the possibility of greater payloads, satellites will be multiple-purpose, carrying equipment for fulfilling a variety of missions. Ultimately, as described earlier, satellites will be very massive and will be periodically staffed by commuting astronauts. These orbital servicemen will be able to repair defective equipment aboard an earth station. They will also be able to tow new parts to the station and enlarge the "observatory."

Any satellite cruising through terrestrial space can "look" up, down and around. The upward or outward look is largely a scientific one without much promise of immediate practical benefits to men on earth, even though the data obtained will be of prime interest to scientists. Survey of the space environment itself comes in the same category, so we are left with the downward look and it is this orbital view which promises to be of the most value for the peacetime applications of earth satellites.

The most obvious, and by all odds the easiest, thing for an orbital device to "see" is the degree of cloud cover veiling the globe. Relatively crude orbital "eyes" composed of cameras and electronic gadgets can also report on the approximate structure, i.e., detail of the cloud mantle covering the earth. In addition, instruments can measure the "heat budget" of the earth and atmosphere so that scientists can determine the exchange of heat energy between the earth and space.

Measurements made by meteorologists on the earth's surface do not provide a global or complete picture of the world's weather. Only a fraction of the globe is sampled by earthbound weather observers and the data require a vast communication network for collection and a considerable staff of experts for analysis. Furthermore, there are a number of measurements which can not be made effectively on the earth's surface. For example, the atmospheric mantle absorbs much of the solar radiation which is incident at the top. By the time the sun's rays filter down through the mixture of atmospheric gases, water vapor and dust particles—a type of perpetual global smog—the identity of the radiation has been altered. Meteorologists are concerned with learning the constancy of the sun's heat output and particularly how the fluctuations vary with time. They also want to know the make-up of the solar radiation, i.e., the infra-red, visible and ultraviolet rays and how these change with time. And they seek to learn how changes on or in the sun affect the earth's weather and climate.

Meteorologists, before the advent of satellites, were forced to make their measurements at the bottom of the atmospheric sea or to rely upon momentary forays made with balloon-borne instruments for sampling the upper air. With the development of satellite weather stations, there came the opportunity to get "on top" of the weather and to record large weather systems on magnetic tape, which was then scanned electronically and tele-vised to earth stations.

Tiros I, the first U.S. experimental weather satellite, went into orbit on April 8, 1960. The 270-pound pillbox-shaped device was shot into a good circular orbit about 445 miles distant from the earth at an angle of 48 degrees inclination to the Equator. Arrays of solar cells, totaling 9,200 in all, powered the device, which included two TV cameras. One camera equipped with a wide-angle lens took a series of pictures covering a strip 800 miles in width while the other, fitted with a narrow-angle lens, took pictures 80 miles on a side. The picture images were stored on magnetic tape until the satellite passed over earth stations de-signed to pick up the Tiros signals. Two ground stations at Fort Monmouth, New Jersey, and Kaena Point, Hawaii, re-ceived the signals and displayed the data on kinescopes where it was viewed visually and also photographed.

Tiros I was the first in a series of weather satellites bearing the initial title "Television, Infrared Observation Satellite," and as such it was a relatively crude device. For example, it was spin-stabilized so that it spun on its axis, but did not always point to the earth. Viewing was done when the cameras did point to the earth and when the earth was in sunlight. Even so, many useful photographs were obtained; for example, one showed a typhoon off Australia.

Satellites in the Tiros series are the forerunners of more sophisticated weather reconnaissance devices known as Nimbus satellites. The 650-pound Nimbus, illustrated in Plate 26, derives its power from a set of solar paddle wheels which swing into position after injection into orbit. The average power generated is 200 watts per orbital trip. A polar orbit at a 600-mile altitude assures global coverage for the satellite. Nimbus contains stabilizing systems designed to keep the device pointed toward the earth at all times. Furthermore, roll, yaw and pitch are controlled to an accuracy of one degree. This is achieved through the combined use of pneumatic jets for coarse control and inertial wheels (gyroscopic effect) for fine adjustment.

Nimbus satellites carry improved television cameras for photographing the cloud cover during the day and a special device for observing events such as hurricanes. In addition, the weather satellite employs an infrared-sensitive device for observation of night time cloud cover. Sensory devices aimed at the sun measure the output of ultraviolet and other solar radiation.

The stationing of three satellites in 24-hour, properly spaced orbits will make it possible to survey the earth almost completely. This 24-hour orbit keeps the satellite in step with a point on the earth's surface. Such an orbit is attained if the satellite moves in a circular path 22,300 miles above the earth. If launched at the Equator in a direction eastward and parallel to the Equator, the satellite will appear to a ground observer as though it were stationary. Some punsters have coined the term "stayputnik" to apply to this equatorial, 24-hour satellite. Should the satellite be injected into an orbit intersecting the equatorial plane at an angle, then it will appear to "walk up and down" or move north and south along a meridian.

A satellite is put into a 24-hour orbit by shooting it on an elliptical orbit such that its apogee is 26,300 miles from the center of the earth. Then at this distance the satellite is given additional rocket thrust parallel to the earth's surface so that it is kicked into a circular orbit. Satellites in a 24-hour orbit are obviously of value for communications, both military and civilian. The Defense Department has Project Decree, which aims at a system of global "real-time" radio relays using three satellites. The term "real-time" is used in communications, both for radio and television signals, to mean that there is no delay introduced as in storage and playback of messages. Project Decree makes use of three "stationary" satellites to provide good coverage of the earth's surface. Project Aeros aims at using "stationary" satellites for weather surveys.

Communications systems linked to 24-hour satellites of the "active-repeater" type (signal received and beamed back to earth by space-borne electronics) pose greater difficulties than those geared to stations in lower orbits. For one thing, for a given rocket power, much smaller payloads can be hoisted to a 24-hour orbit altitude. For another, the great distance between earth and the satellite increases the power requirements both for the ground and the orbital relay station.

Project Courier, under the technical direction of the U.S. Army's Signal Corps, is designed to explore some of the technical problems associated with global, orbital communications. Courier satellites, such as those launched in 1960, are normally placed in a 600-mile-high orbit. The satellite weighs 500 pounds and carries 19,200 solar cells banked around its waist. This power supply feeds into an array of 300 pounds of electrical gadgets including four receivers and four transmitters as well as five tape recorders. Courier is a "delayed repeater" rather than a real-time communications system; it receives, stores and then plays back information. Monitoring posts at Fort Monmouth, N. J., and at the Army Space Communication Center near Ponce, Puerto Rico, employ 28-foot dish antennas in tracking the Courier satellites. The initial communication system has a capacity of 68,000 coded words per minute. Actually, Project Courier is an outgrowth of Project Score—the "talking Atlas" which broadcast President Eisenhower's Christmas message of 1958.

NASA is watching with interest the application of military satellites to communications, especially of the active-repeater type. The Defense Department began its work on Project Notus

—the over-all code name for satellite communications—before the establishment of NASA, and remains in charge of the projects, such as Courier and Decree, because of the military requirement for reliable global communications. The satellite systems appeal to the military because they offer greater freedom from interference—whether natural or man-made "jamming" —and they have advantages over existing global communications.

For example, the Defense Department's Project Steer is a satellite project designed to utilize a system of five or six devices in proper spacings along a polar orbit. Each satellite, orbiting at an altitude of 5,600 miles, receives messages broadcast from ground stations and rebroadcasts these to aircraft operating in the polar areas. The aircraft then use the same radio link for reply.

The Defense Department is spending approximately $50 million per year on communications satellites. This amount will probably be increased sharply by 1965, when ambitious projects such as Decree become operational. Successful application of the Decree-type 24-hour satellite has the potential of handling 300 voice channels simultaneously. This represents a tenfold higher capacity than the best cable connections across the Atlantic. Laying of transoceanic cable is very expensive and provides only limited traffic capacity. Yet overseas telephone messages are mounting sharply—some six million are expected in 1964. And transocean cables are technically incapable of carrying a television signal. Commenting on space communications, Dr. Lloyd Berkner, a top U.S. advisor, predicted:

Intercontinental radio and television networks are elementary examples of the applications of space communications that should be available in the next decade or so. World-wide telephone dialing will become possible. Message costs will be cut to perhaps one-tenth their present levels.

Apart from cutting communications costs, the advent of a new development, such as global television, can have immense impact upon society. Of course, there are some who would maintain that global TV would set civilization back many years, and considering the quality of many U.S. programs, this is probably no exaggeration. But with the proper use of the new medium, there is the possibility of linking the darkest jungle village or the loneliest Arctic outpost with the rest of the world. Thus technology offers a unifying, a cohesive and a constructive bond for men the world over. The real-time telecasting of events on a global scale is an exciting prospect for the future. Furthermore, the elimination of the present line-of-sight or horizon barrier for TV reception should open up every nation to signals beamed down from orbital stations.

While the Defense Department has pioneered in active-repeater communications satellites, NASA has devoted great effort to the development of passive or reflecting orbital devices. Plate 27 illustrates the variety of reflectors which are candidates for passive earth-orbital relaying of messages. On August 12, 1960, Echo I, a 100-foot-diameter inflated plastic sphere was shot into a good circular orbit at a distance of roughly 1,000 miles. The sphere is made up of Mylar plastic so thin that it weighs only 132 pounds. Four pounds of aluminum, vapor-deposited on the plastic, provide the reflecting surface needed to bounce high-frequency (20,000-megacycle) radio waves back to earth. The carefully folded balloon was packed in a 26-inch-diameter magnesium sphere along with a sublimating chemical. The chemical changes readily from a solid to a gas and provides the pressure needed to inflate the balloon in space. In order to guard against overinflation some 200 pinpricks were made in the plastic.

Echo I, traveling six miles every second, reflected the sun's light down to earth, where it was observed by most everyone on the globe, since the orbit was inclined at an angle of 47 degrees to the Equator. This meant that almost everyone (except polar explorers in the Antarctic) in the Southern Hemisphere saw the satellite, which appeared in the sky as a star of first magnitude. In the Northern Hemisphere, Echo I was visible as far north as Montreal, Canada. Brighter than the North Star, Echo I made an orbital circuit once every two hours. In many locations it remained in view for ten minutes, moving in a segmented arc across the heavens. Echo I was so large and so light that the gentle push of the sun's rays—a small fraction of an ounce—perturbed its orbit.

The passive satellites, like Echo, have the great advantage that they are essentially mechanical and simple as opposed to electronic devices. This not only reduces cost, but it insures reliability through simplicity of construction and, with further development, allows for long life. Furthermore, the radio mirror in space is freely available to any nation wishing to bounce signals off it. In contrast, active-repeaters of the Courier-Steer-Decree type are complex, require considerable power, and operate only on certain radio frequencies and, in some cases, handle coded traffic. They tend to have a short life, but more than compensating for this drawback is the fact that they can amplify the signals they receive and beam them back to earth. This procedure simplifies power requirements for earth transmitters.

Development of orbital or space communications makes it mandatory that the nations of the world reach agreement on the allocation of certain radio frequencies to space vehicles. Interference between satellites must be avoided and reception should not be marred by local disturbances caused by industrial uses of high-frequency devices. Unfortunately, the radio-frequency spectrum is getting quite crowded owing to the many uses for radio waves, and the clearing of channels solely for space communications has become an urgent problem.

Another use for both military and peacetime satellites is as orbital devices for navigation. The U.S. Navy has pioneered in this field with its Project Transit. Objectives of the Transit program are to provide mobile surface vessels and aircraft with an improved capability for navigation of high precision, global coverage, simplicity and all-weather operation. By virtue of the fact that a satellite of proved design has highly predictable orbits, there is the possibility of using it as a sentinel. The principle involved is that of using a transmitter aboard the satellite and controlling its radio frequency precisely. Ships at sea or aircraft, observing the fast-moving transmitter, can through the use of electronic devices and the known orbit of the satellite fix their relative positions. A change in frequency, due to the motion of the source, is observed; this is the Doppler effect which is familiar to anyone who has listened to the pitch (frequency) of a train whistle as the train approaches and recedes. Navy experts believe that a total of four Transit satellites, circulating in polar orbits, will provide accurate navigational aids. Improvements in observing equipment, probable before 1965, should permit an earth observer to fix his position to an accuracy of less than a quarter-mile. Further refinements look toward an eventual accuracy of 100 yards.

Transit satellites were first launched successfully in 1960. Experiments associated with Transit II-A, launched June 22, 1960, involved the simultaneous injection into orbit of two satellites (Plate 28, Fig. 9), the first time such a feat was accomplished. One experiment furthered by Transit experience aims at increasing the accuracy of geodetic measurements.

Vanguard I proved to be a useful device for measuring the shape of the earth. The term "shape" does not mean the profile of the earth's surface, marked as it is by mountainous extremes and flat deserts. Rather it refers to what is called the geoid, or the surface of mean sea level. Before Vanguard I, geodetic experts knew that the geoid was not a perfect sphere. They described it as an "ellipsoid of revolution"; this was the technical way of describing the fact that the earth bulges in places. By analysis of "perturbations" or small changes in the orbital characteristics of Vanguard I, scientists deduced that the earth was slightly pear-shaped. Actually the deviations are quite small, being 25- and 50-foot bulges. An important conclusion deriving from the Vanguard data is that the earth's structure is stronger or more rigid than had been thought earlier.

A geodetic satellite holds promise of adding considerably to our knowledge of geodesy. It is quite small and compact and features a high-intensity flashing light or beacon which can be observed optically from earth stations. The broadcasting of precise time signals from the geodetic satellite, together with photography of the beacon light against a background of the

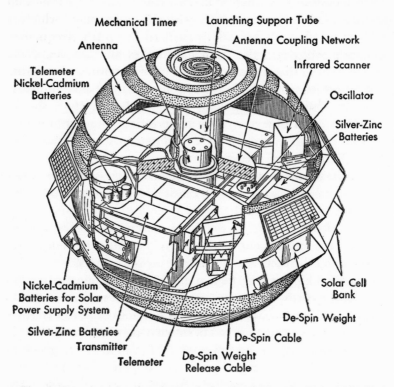

Fig. 9. Drawing showing internal detail of Transit II-A. *U.S. Navy*

stars, gives a three-position measurement (star, observer, and satellite) so necessary to geodetic triangulation. (This is the basic method of establishing a geodetic network on the earth's surface and for measuring earth distances.) Triangulation networks on our continent allow positions to be fixed to an accuracy of 25 yards over a distance of 3,000 miles. When one ventures off the continent, there is less accuracy because of the absence of a short base line to use in triangulation and as a result the location of some major islands and the separation of continents is poorly known. Use of the geodetic satellite should make possible the extension of precise geodetic measurements to the entire globe.

We have not exhausted the practical applications for earth satellites with this brief run-down of the possibilities. Many unforeseen uses will probably crop up, once scientists and engineers begin to think in terms of space science. Furthermore, the availability of a more massive satellite will remove the present miser's attitude toward allocating payload only to high-priority tasks.

I feel that it is improper to end this account of earth satellites without at least mentioning a few of the scientific uses to which the orbital devices lend themselves. Some of these may seem far afield from the affairs of the workaday world, but they tantalize scientists who seek fundamental knowledge about the universe.

NASA has plans for a series of scientific satellites to be launched throughout the sixties. An Orbital Astronomical Observatory will orbit a 36-inch telescope which can view stars and planets without the shimmer and dance caused by the earth's atmosphere. Even more important is the fact that OAO observations allow a "full-color" view of the stars. Observations made through telescopes mounted on the earth's surface are severely restricted because the atmosphere blots out much of the light emitted by distant stars. The spectrum, or total range of color, emitted by a star is the foundation stone upon which an astronomer, or more precisely an astrophysicist, builds his concept of stellar structure. Unfortunately, the earth's air mantle obscures the information most desired by the scientist, namely, the far ultraviolet light emitted by the stars. Given an observatory, even a relatively crude one, far above the murk of the earth's atmosphere, the astronomer gets a new view of the universe. Ultimately, as we have already stated in connection with the manned space laboratory, the astronomer-astronaut will be able to man the telescope instead of depending upon televised data or capsule recovery of photographic data.

A scientific satellite devoted to observing the sun is of more than purely academic value. The sun exerts a profound effect upon the earth apart from the obvious fact that its heat-light sustains life on our planet. Solar eccentricities—its periodic changes in heat output, its sudden trantrums which shower the earth with penetrating rays and the spectacular changes in its gaseous mantle—affect our weather, our climate and our communications. So we may expect some practical dividends from solar research, even though the scientist is principally concerned with understanding the sun's basic mechanisms.

Scientists are also deeply concerned with events taking place closer to the earth. They wish to understand the vertical structure of the atmosphere—its changes in temperature, in gas composition and in pressure. And beyond the palpable atmosphere, they wish to learn more about the radiation belts surrounding the earth. One satellite, known as EGO, for Eccentric Geophysical Laboratory, will circuit the earth in a highly elliptical pattern out to a distance of 70,000 miles. Thus it will traverse the multiple radiation belts and telemeter data about them to earth observers. EGO, launched in 1963, is also aimed at studying the earth's magnetic field.

A companion satellite, orbiting at lower altitude and in a polar orbit, is designated POGO, for Polar Orbital Geophysical Observatory. Both EGO and POGO satellites have high payloads and carry a cargo of many different kinds of instruments.

Physicists are anxious to put in orbit a "time experiment" which is designed to verify the effect of gravity upon a clock. According to Einstein's General Theory of Relativity, gravitational force should produce an effect upon the rate at which a clock runs. A satellite clock should run faster than one on earth and it should speed up as the orbital clock is sent farther from our planet. The speed-up is, however, quite small, about one second in a century for a clock orbited at an altitude of 4,000 miles.

Recent advances in nuclear science allow for the measurement of extremely small time intervals. As a result, scientists are optimistic that the Einstein time experiment can be performed in orbit. The basic concept of the experiment is the comparison of two clocks, identical in timekeeping precision, one of which is put into orbit and the other kept on earth. The comparison is somewhat complicated by the fact that the motion of the orbital clock tends to slow it down. Einstein's Special Theory of Relativity established that the faster an object moves, the slower is time measured in the moving system. This effect is usually quite negligible except at very high speeds (far above orbital velocities) at which the moving object approaches the speed of light—186,000 miles per second. Theoretically, time stands still as one reaches this velocity. At orbital speeds the effect is comparable to that of gravity acting at modest altitudes —but it acts in the opposite way so that the two effects cancel out at an altitude of about 2,000 miles. Above this neutralizing zone, a satellite clock should speed up owing to the weakened gravity, and measurement of this small effect will be a dual triumph—a masterful experimental coup and a resounding success confirming Einstein's predictions.

The development of the Saturn, with its capacity for hurling massive devices into orbit, and the entry of man into space will add a new dimension to the experiments and applications that can be made with earth satellites. The construction of permanent earth stations equipped with many tons of equipment and boasting nuclear power plants for generating electricity is a project that can be fulfilled before 1970. If possible, this permanent earth station ought to be an international project. There should be no sovereignty in space.

As the earth's satellite population grows, there is not likely to be much of a traffic problem; that is: there is so much space that collisions are most improbable. But after a period of time many of the orbital devices will be "dead" and will be a nuisance to those on the ground who have to track orbital objects. This means that some type of garbage collection will be in order.

Depending upon the nature of the orbital garbage, it could be towed to a central depot (for parts could be reclaimed), kicked out of orbit to burn up in the atmosphere or refitted with new parts by astronauts operating from a maneuverable spaceship.

9

MILITARY SPACE VEHICLES

SOME SPACE EXPERTS conceive of near-earth space as a possible future battleground. I do not include the non-orbital flight of ICBM's as coming within the domain of "space war," nor do I accept the Buck Rogers style of spaceship conflicts in outer space. The present potentialities of space technology rule out manned spaceships as military vehicles in the near future. I mean maneuverable spaceships cruising in orbital patterns for the purpose of delivering or intercepting nuclear weapons. I believe that orbital H-bomb carriers, circling the earth in readiness to be "called down" on target, are a possibility. Their military worth is debatable, although few would question the terror potential of such weapons.

There are military space vehicles under development which will be in orbit in the mid-sixties. These include satellites designed to gather weather data, to provide reliable communications and to aid in navigation; they may either coincide with the satellites already discussed or they may be specifically military projects. In addition to such satellites, the Defense Department has under way a number of high priority projects designed to provide surveillance of enemy targets or facilities and also to give early warning of missile attack. These come under the code names Discoverer, Samos and Midas.

Midas has no connection with the King of Phrygia, whose touch turned everything to gold. It stands for "Missile Defense Alarm Satellite." The Air Research and Development Command of the U.S. Air Force began work on Midas in November of 1958. The objective of Midas is, to quote from official documents: "the development of the capability to provide continuous screening of worldwide launchings of ballistic missiles through the detection of the infrared emanations from the associated exhaust plume during the powered ascent of the missile(s). In this manner, through instantaneous reporting by the satellite to a ground station which relays data to the appropriate operational forces, maximum warning can be obtained regarding a hostile missile attack."

In less technical language, Midas is a project aimed at keeping in orbit a number of satellites equipped with sensitive eyes to detect ICBM firings. The project is tied in with fear of surprise attack and is aimed at giving a half-hour warning of an oncoming salvo of rockets. Midas is, in effect, an infrared picket fence in space.

Samos is the name of a small Greek island in the Aegean Sea; it is apparently also a code name, picked at random, as a successor to more descriptive names (Big Brother, Pied Piper and Sentry) which were given to Project WS-117L. The idea for a reconnaissance satellite, or "orbital spy in the sky," was first proposed in 1946. It was mentioned as a possibility in the next few years by Secretary of Defense Forrestal, but then the idea lay dormant. A contract for Weapons System-117L, or "New Horizon," was awarded to the Lockheed Aircraft Corporation and research was started in July of 1955. Its official mission is given: "Our objective is to develop a reconnaissance satellite system capable of providing reconnaissance information which will permit photographic coverage of selected areas of the earth."

Project Discoverer is aimed at paving the way for both Midas and Samos. Even though they have different functions and operate in different orbits and have dissimilar payloads, Midas and Samos have certain basic requirements in common. Project Discoverer has as its purpose the launching of 38 test vehicles designed to demonstrate the feasibility of guiding, controlling, stabilizing and communicating with satellites. And in the case of Samos, there is the additional objective of recovering capsules ejected from the space vehicle.

Discoverer satellites have been shot into orbit from the Pacific Missile Range (Point Mugu, California) and attempts have been made to recover the ejected capsules, using aircraft equipped with trapeze-type catching gear. The sequence in the launch-orbit-recovery operation is as follows. Launching is accomplished through the use of a first-stage Thor rocket which generates 165,000 pounds of thrust. Then, at a height of 82 miles, the second stage is ignited; this consists of a Lockheed Agena rocket weighing about four tons. After burn-out the separated second stage weighs 1,600 pounds (Plate 29). This vehicle is shot into a polar orbit several hundred miles above sea level. This procedure was followed successfully many times during 1959 and 1960 but it was not until Discoverer XIII was orbited that complete success attended the operation.

Discoverer XIII was injected into orbit at an altitude of 161 miles and after the Agena engine was cut off, high-pressure pneumatic jets stabilized the attitude of the vehicle. It made 17 orbits, ranging out to a maximum of 436 miles, and somewhere over the North Pole a command triggered small gas jets, tilting the vehicle 60 degrees toward earth. The orbit-ejection system, built by the General Electric Company, actuated explosive bolts and springs separating the re-entry vehicle from its parent capsule. A retrorocket was fired immediately, slowing the package to less than orbital speed. The re-entry vehicle began a gradual descent into the atmosphere and the trajectory became more and more nearly vertical as it neared the earth.

At an altitude of 50,000 feet a parachute snapped out of the re-entry package and slowed its downward flight. By this time the package, originally 300 pounds in weight, had lost its retro-rocket and parachute cover and part of its heat shield had been evaporated by the 4,000° F. heat which built up at the surface of the protective covering; it was reduced to 85 pounds. A C-119 Flying Boxcar missed intercepting the drifting space device and it plunged into the Pacific Ocean about 330 miles northwest of Honolulu. A Navy frogman lowered to the spot by helicopter snared the submerged capsule. The recovery on August 11, 1960, marked the first recapture of an orbital device. An 18-by-24-inch American flag with fifty stars was sealed inside the Discoverer capsule. The latter has been presented to the Smithsonian Institution for permanent display in Washington, D.C.

The very next shot in the Discoverer series achieved all its objectives including the final snaring of the parachute-supported capsule by a C-119 aircraft. The plane made two passes narrowly missing each time, and on the third try, its nylon recovery gear intercepted the Discoverer payload. This was then winched into the bay of the Flying Boxcar.

Midas II, the first successful prototype flight of an infrared orbital device, was sent into an almost circular orbit (perigee: 292 miles; apogee: 322 miles) on May 24, 1960. Launched by an Atlas booster and accelerated to 17,045 mph by an Agena-A second-stage engine, the device weighed 5,000 pounds. Almost 3,000 pounds of complex instrumentation was carried in the 22-foot-long, five-foot-diameter satellite (Plate 30). Midas II was shot into an orbit which inclined at an angle of 33 degrees to the Equator. Thus its trajectory was apparently fixed in order to avoid having the satellite crisscross the Soviet Union. When the perfected Midas vehicles become operational sometime in 1963 they will be sent into high polar orbits, over 1,500 miles above sea level. The development of the Agena-B restartable space engine will permit placing the Midas in precise orbits since it will be possible to add small thrusts to nudge the gadget into the desired trajectory. It is estimated that at least six Midas vehicles, spaced in preassigned orbits, will be required to insure adequate and continuous coverage of the Soviet Union's launching sites.

Midas detection gear will be actuated only when making passes over Soviet territory so that power is conserved. Should any Midas fail in operation, stand-by vehicles will be launched into orbit to replace the "missing link" in the infrared picket fence. The Midas program cost about $100 million during 1960 and it is estimated that it will run to twice this figure during the early sixties. Additional funds will be required to link the Midas detection system with a reliable means of global communication.

Ground-based radars, such as the three huge "big dish" installations in the Arctic and in Great Britain, constitute the heart of the present BMEWS, or Ballistic Missiles Early Warning System. These football-field-sized radars scan for ballistic missiles as they reach a peak altitude, some 600 miles above sea level, and begin their downward trajectories. Some 12 to 15 minutes of early warning are possible with the BMEWS radars. Midas detection in orbit essentially doubles this warning time. A question can be raised about the reason and urgency for the Midas system.

Lt. Gen. Bernard A. Schriever, commander of the Air Research and Development Command, provided the military requirement for Midas when he explained (quoted from a speech on "The Military Role in Space" given March 10, 1960, at the Institute of Aeronautical Sciences):

The advent of megaton-yield nuclear weapons, of supersonic airplanes, of ballistic missiles, and the space age, has caused the world to shrink in terms of time to a mere fraction of its former size. This compression of the time factor has given a new and ominous definition to the element of surprise.

It is no exaggeration to say that the United States is haunted by the fear of an attack "coming out of the blue." Twenty-five or thirty minutes of warning would permit aircraft of the Strategic Air Command to become air-borne. Thus the striking power of the U.S. retaliatory effort could be retained and the foreknowledge of this fact would lend credibility to the deterrent power of the United States.

The Defense Department has assigned the highest priority (DX or 0.01 urgency rating) to Project Samos. Together with Projects Discoverer and Midas, over $1 billion has been spent on orbital devices in the first three years of the space era. Expenditures for Project Samos will increase until the mid-sixties when it is expected that a series of the reconnaissance vehicles will be operational. Samos vehicles will orbit in the 150-to-300-mile range of altitude in order to obtain good surveillance detail. Some missions will probably be quite brief for detailed survey of localized areas of interest; others will orbit for longer periods of time and relay data back to earth either through a series of ejected capsules—similar to Discoverer XIII—or by slow transmission of television pictures.

The purpose of Samos reconnaissance is essentially the same as that of the much-discussed U-2 flights over Russia. It is to provide detailed intelligence data about Soviet military activities, such as weapons production and installations. Included in the "most wanted" list of targets for Samos cameras is data on ICBM sites, communication centers, air defense centers and missile production plants. The U-2 aircraft built by Lockheed Aircraft Corporation, the same firm given the Samos project, flew a limited number of deep-penetration missions over the U.S.S.R. during the 1956-60 period prior to the May Day flight when a U-2 was brought down inside Russia. The U-2 flew at altitudes of about 70,000 feet and photographed a strip of Soviet territory roughly 100 miles in width. Precision cameras aboard the U-2 took detailed photographs which permitted intelligence specialists to identify various types of aircraft parked on airstrips. It is claimed that the KS-25 reconnaissance camera, developed by Fairchild Camera and Instrument Corporation, can resolve two-foot-diameter objects on the ground at altitudes of 100,000 feet and for aircraft speeds of over 1,000 mph.

A camera "hung in the sky" at an altitude of, say, 150 miles will produce a photograph of the earth below whose coverage, i.e., terrain area, depends upon the focal length of the lens used. A three-foot-focal-length lens could project onto a 70-mm. film an image of a ten-mile-wide strip 150 miles below the camera. With good resolution in the system, it should be possible to discern objects 12 feet on a side. It is interesting to note that our hypothetical camera "hung in the sky" would, in a satellite such as Samos, be moving with very high speed. This makes it necessary to shorten the exposure time to as little as 1/5,000 of a second; otherwise the image will be blurred. Extremely sensitive film of high resolving power is an essential for satellite photography. Longer focal lengths are desirable for fineness of detail, but this increases the size of the camera and makes it necessary to carry large amounts of film. Cameras with a 12-foot focal length have been developed for the U.S. Air Force. It seems reasonable that camera systems for satellite observation will be developed to a point where an eight-foot-square object may be perceived on the ground.

The principal problem with Samos reconnaissance is not to get the camera over the target or take the pictures; it is rather the relaying of the picture data back to earth. The situation is much the same as that in conventional espionage, where you may succeed in planting an agent in a key missile plant but then wind up by having immense difficulty in communicating with him. Data from a Samos satellite can be received either in the form of photographic films ejected in recoverable capsules or in the form of television pictures. The photographic film recovery has the advantage of providing a great deal of data in a single package but it is limited in other respects. Sheer weight of film is a factor; so, too, is the risk of failure in recovery and the limited time of operation of the satellite. The development of a multiple ejector (nicknamed the "orbital six-shooter") for

Samos will add to the value of the film-recovery technique. Television reception is certainly possible but the amount of information transmittable from orbit is sharply limited by the transmitting capacity of the television channel. Since a ground station can receive for only about ten minutes, when the transmitter is in range, this constitutes a further limitation.

Suppose that a Samos satellite manages to take good photographs of three million square miles of territory. This corresponds to an area the size of the United States. Suppose further that this photographic film is of high resolution and consists of half a mile of 4.5-inch film. It would take 1,200 hours of transmission time to broadcast the information, but since only certain portions of the satellite's trajectory are favorable for transmission and since one has a limited number of ground stations within range of orbit, the actual time consumed in the television of the data would run into years. However, where photographs only of special interest were wanted, the television technique would be useful.

General Schriever looks forward to a time when Samos satellites may be supplemented or replaced by manned orbital vehicles. Referring to reconnaissance satellites, he predicted: "Eventually, too, we will place pilots and observers in them—there are many activities for which a human flyer is better fitted than the most sensitive instrument." Naturally, a manned observation satellite would have to be much more massive in order to provide the life-support system for the observer. But as powerful booster rockets become available and astronauts gain experience in orbital flight, large orbital craft with human observers will become feasible for military reconnaissance. The great advantage of having a man at the controls of the camera, or viewing the earth with a telescope, is that he can exercise judgment and discretion in the selection of ground areas to be scanned. On the other hand, the great payload required for life-support and re-entry of an astronaut convinces some experts that manned reconnaissance spacecraft is a dubious military venture.

The intelligence-seeking Samos and, more futuristically, the advent of manned, orbital vehicles raise questions about national sovereignty. Both legal and military problems are involved. The Soviets raised grave objections to U-2 overflights, once they had either the ability or the good fortune to arrest such an espionage mission. They argued that it was a gross violation of international law for the United States to intrude upon the sovereign territory of the Soviet Union. In this case, it was contended, sovereignty extended up to U-2 altitudes. On the other hand, the Soviets were the first to send massive orbital devices around the world. Could they then advance the claim that Samos missions violate their sovereign rights?

As long as nations surround their military orbital missions with a shroud of secrecy, there would be no way of ascertaining the "hostility" of a satellite. The charge could be made that it was equipped for espionage or even housed a nuclear weapon. Allegations made on the latter score would be sure to find a sympathetic reception among neighboring countries, whereas a charge of espionage would meet with closed ears.

Legal experts have now concerned themselves with the intricacies of space law. Any body of law derives from precedent and custom, but there is little of either to throw light on rules for outer space. One can search through the past and here it seems that domestic law in both the U.S. and U.S.S.R. converge to a common understanding. The Soviets see no limit to sovereignty in the upward direction. Anglo-American law holds to the maxim: *cuius est solum, eius est usque ad coelum,* or "he who owns the land owns it up to the sky." Any interpretation of space law hinges upon the subtle point—where does space begin?

One might define certain limits, as, for example, an upper limit to the atmosphere as that altitude where aerodynamic or winged flight ceases. A lower limit for space could be the minimum altitude for orbital or satellite flight. Unfortunately, these limits are not precise and they will be further blurred by new developments in technology. The Dynasoar or a hybrid spacecraft may erase previously defined limits.

Even after agreement is reached, if this is possible, the matter will probably be academic. Many lawyers have long held that sovereignty really depends upon control. A nation could claim that a space vehicle violated its sovereignty, but unless it was able to control the region—by bringing force to bear—the violation could not be punished except by sanctions applied elsewhere. It is noteworthy that a number of U-2 overflights were observed by the Soviets, but no protest was lodged before May 1, 1960.

Assuming that a Samos or some other reconnaissance spacecraft were regarded by the Soviets as trespassing upon sovereign territory, the Kremlin would gain little by sending similar space vehicles over the United States. The openness of the U.S.A. serves to defeat the purpose of a Soviet Samos mission. If the Soviets regarded the intrusion of U.S. orbital devices as serious, meaning that their military security was compromised, they might do more than lodge diplomatic protests or launch a propaganda campaign. The Soviet Union has a technological option. It could undertake the development of an antisatellite weapon.

Anyone familiar with the pessimism surrounding the development of an antimissile rocket as a defense against ICBM's may wonder why some scientists believe that an apparently much more difficult feat of technology can be accomplished. In the case of intercepting an ICBM the problem is made exceedingly complex by the very little time available for determining the ICBM's course, alerting missile centers and for directing and firing the rockets. Once a satellite is sent into orbit, ground tracking stations can determine its trajectory with precision and computers can then predict the exact position of the "intruder" at any time in the future. This is certainly an advantage since it gives ground crews time to ready powerful rockets. Rocket experts can also program the course to be followed by the interceptor. A number of possibilities exist for intercepting and "killing" the hostile object in orbit. A sounding rocket, shooting straight up, could, in theory, arrive at the invader's orbital altitude a split second before the satellite and loose a screen of sand shrapnel. A satellite encountering this projectile cloud would be severely damaged, for it would be exactly the same as though the satellite were stationary and received a violent bombardment with sand projectiles traveling at 18,000 miles per hour.

The timing for vertical interception of an object in orbit is exquisite and it may be more feasible to shoot at the offender from an orbital path. For example, the antisatellite device might be injected into an orbit almost identical with that of the enemy vehicle. It would require almost incredible precision to score a hit directly, but from the vantage point of proximity to the intruder, small rockets could be launched to home in on the target. The object would be to maim or disable or blind the instruments aboard the satellite. One does not "shoot down" a satellite. Since there is practically no air at orbital altitudes, the blast from exposive weapons is very limited; however, shrapnel and heat effects may be destructive.

Antisatellite weapons require a highly sophisticated technology that is not presently available. Furthermore, it is very probable that satellite-killers will be long-term developments. It would appear, however, that the Soviets have a military requirement for such a weapons system and that the weapon might emerge from its technological cocoon later in this decade.

If we look ahead to the day of manned orbital flight and envisage human observers in military reconnaissance vehicles, and if we assume that the Soviets will elect to interdict such missions, we enter upon the weird phase of manned combat in near-earth space. Killing a spaceman in orbit is a much easier task than disabling his vehicle. Human beings are quite vulnerable to penetrating radiation such as that emitted by a nuclear-weapon detonation. The radiation flash from a high-power nuclear blast could have a lethal effect upon satellite occupants some 30 miles away. More in the true line of Buck Rogers is the space or ray gun which projects a beam of atomic particles across many miles of space. Such weapons may seem fanciful at present but they are by no means beyond the power of technology. In fact, a company in Texas has undertaken serious investigation of ray-gun devices.

An antisatellite capability would be extremely valuable if orbital weapons carriers become a reality. Dr. Herbert F. York, director of Defense Research and Engineering, stated on March 30, 1960, that: "There is no development program to build a bombardment satellite." But he also indicated that work on the Discoverer program paralleled work that would be necessary to develop a satellite carrier for nuclear weapons. Apart from the terror aspect, an orbital bomber would have the advantage of providing an almost invulnerable bomb base, as long as the enemy did not develop an antisatellite weapon. All land or sea bases for ballistic missiles have a degree of vulnerability to surprise attack. Fixed ICBM bases, like those for Atlas and Titan, are vulnerable to enemy attack even though the ICBM's are hidden in concrete fortifications below ground. The Polaris submarine is capable of prolonged submerged cruises but it, too, is subject to technological innovations that might see powerful antisubmarine weapons developed.

An orbiting H-bomb has a maximum of mobility and thus a minimum of vulnerability. It has two additional advantages— salvo capability and recallability. In effect, weapons in orbit are already launched and they can therefore be looked upon as having assured salvo strength. When we consider that many ICBM's would have to be launched on a few minutes' notice, this salvo feature of orbital bombs is important. Just as significant is the fact that a weapon in orbit can be recalled whereas an ICBM, once launched, is committed to its mission. But it has obvious and some serious drawbacks, especially for the United States. Unless a special launching site were selected, say in the far Pacific, residents of the U.S.A. would voice loud objections to rockets being launched within the U.S.A. where missile malfunctions might bring down a nuclear weapon upon home soil. Orbital H-bombs would have to be equipped with foolproof and long-lasting controls. We would have to be able to kick them out of orbit and land them upon selected targets with a high degree of accuracy. Considerations such as these convince a number of weapons experts that an orbital weapons system does not promise a sufficiently great improvement over the land-based or ocean-based ICBM to be worth the immense national effort required to perfect it. About the most that one can say in summing up the military potential of space weapons is that it will be a number of years before their worth can be evaluated with any degree of reliability. Meanwhile, however, the risks of being upset by new technological developments forces competing nations to explore new weapons systems carefully.

Since most military space vehicles will come under the category of "dark objects," meaning that they do not emit distinguishing signals, it is clearly a military requirement that all dark satellites be kept in perpetual inventory. That is to say, it is important to track such vehicles and to keep them accounted for. The Defense Department has established Project Shepherd for this purpose. It consists of two parts, the first being Spasur (space surveillance) which is a series of detection posts strung across the southern U.S.A. This satellite detection fence detects, tracks and identifies silent, "dead" or unco-operative satellites. The second part is the establishment of a National Space Surveillance and Control Center at Hascom Air Force Base, Bedford, Massachusetts, where tabs will be kept on all satellites of interest. Early phases of this work are being carried out at the Cambridge Air Force Research Center in Massachusetts.

Ground surveillance of satellites can give some data about the characteristics of the space vehicles. However, there is no way of determining whether a massive orbital device is "hostile" in the sense that it might be a bomb carrier. Samos-type space devices might be partially identified but this would depend upon the mode of operation of the satellite, i.e., whether intelligence data were transmitted by television to ground stations.

The potential military value of space and the difficulty of inspecting orbital vehicles lends urgency to the need for reaching some agreement upon international control of space. The best way to insure that hostile objects do not go into orbit would be to agree upon United Nations inspection of all space vehicles prior to launch. This inspection problem is simple to prescribe but infinitely difficult to solve in practice since nations will be most reluctant to allow U.N. inspection of military vehicles. U.S. defense officials would probably be opposed to letting U.N. inspectors look at vehicles of the Samos type. Soviet military men would undoubtedly be against letting foreigners view their rockets and launch installations. Thus "space inspection" is a problem shot through with as many difficulties as the technical aspects of a ban on nuclear tests.

War has been made vastly more complex by the advent of the space age. Space vehicles are still not sufficiently developed for us to discern the future patterns of space warfare. While we can dismiss armed conflict in outer space, there appear to be numerous military applications for space vehicles in near-earth space.

10

PROBES AND PLANETS

OUR SOLAR SYSTEM includes a family of nine planets, all
of which sweep around the central sun in the same direction.
Mercury, the "winged messenger," speeds about the sun once
every 88 days in a tight elliptical orbit averaging 36 million miles
in radius. Pluto, the outermost member of the family, rides in
a deep, elongated orbit whose rim is an average of 3.3 billion
miles from our sun. There is thus a hundred-fold difference
between the distances from the sun of our closest and farthest
planet.

We define the plane in which the earth moves about the sun
as the ecliptic; most of the planets move within a few degrees
of this plane. Pluto, the outrider, rocks up and down in its orbit
more steeply. A summary of the planetary characteristics appears
in Table I. There is an orderly increase in the period of revolution for the planets, ranging from 88 days for Mercury to 247
years for Pluto. There is also a continuing drop-off in planet

TABLE I: OUR SOLAR SYSTEM

	Mercury	Venus	Earth	Mars	Jupiter	Saturn	Uranus	Neptune	Pluto
Distance from Sun (millions of miles)	36	67	93	142	484	887	1,785	2,800	3,675
Diameter (thousands of miles)	3.1	7.7	7.9	4.1	87	71	32	31	3.7
Surface Gravity (Earth = 1)	.36	.86	1.0	.40	2.6	1.2	.9	1.1	?
Period of Revolution (years)	.41	.61	1.0	1.9	11.9	29.4	84	165	248
Mass (Earth = 1)	.05	.82	1.0	.11	318	95	14.6	17.3	.83
Volume (Earth = 1)	.06	.92	1.0	.15	1318	736	64	60	1
Mean temperature °F. (* = warmest)	780*	?	60	85*	−230	−290	−340	−360	−375
Inclination to ecliptic (degrees)	7	3.2	—	1.5	1.2	2.3	.5	1.5	18
Period of Rotation (hours)	88 d	?	24	24.3	10	10	11	16	?
Intensity of Sunlight (Earth = 1)	6.7	1.9	1.0	.43	.04	.01	.003	.001	.0006

temperatures as one goes from the innermost to the outermost members of the solar system, where the sun's light dims and its heat is a thousandth that felt on earth.

In this chapter we focus attention upon Mars and Venus, our closest companions. We confine ourselves to the sending of probes—inquisitive rockets armed with guidance equipment and instruments—to explore interplanetary space. These scientific probes substitute for man in this decade. Man's journey to Mars and Venus is postponed to times beyond 1970, when space technology and improved rocket thrust will make manned missions into deep space possible.

Our planet earth cannot be considered stationary with respect to the moving targets Mars and Venus, which we seek to explore. The earth speeds through space at an average velocity of 18.5 miles per second or 66,600 miles per hour. It maintains an average separation from the sun of 93 million miles, but edges three million miles closer in January and a like distance farther away half a year later. In the process, it alternately speeds up and slows down by a thousand miles per hour.

Mars, the diminutive brother of earth, swings about the sun in an ellipse whose closest approach (perihelion) is 128 million miles and whose farthest (aphelion) is 155 million miles. The Martian year is 687 days, during which time Mars averages 15 miles per second in speed, being somewhat more sluggish, as we would expect, since Mars is a satellite of our sun and is farther removed from it than earth. Because it follows an eccentric orbit, Mars speeds up to 16.4 miles per second at perihelion and slows down to 13.6 miles per second at aphelion. This technical detail is of considerable importance for interplanetary trips, since rocket experts pay severe penalties in designing rockets which have to reach very high velocities. It therefore makes a great difference whether one attempts to rendezvous with Mars when it is at aphelion or at perihelion.

Any interplanetary rocket possesses high velocity even though it stands motionless on the launch pad. It shares the 18.5 mile per second velocity of the earth about the sun. Interplanetary travel is effected by adding to or subtracting from this velocity, meaning that the rocket is fired "forward" in the direction of the earth's course about the sun or "backward." In the same way a satellite of the earth can be sent into a higher or lower orbit by applying thrust or retrothrust to it. A complication is introduced by the fact that the rocket we wish to fire to Mars is on the earth's surface; it is not a satellite in space. In order to get the space probe off the earth, we must give it sufficient velocity to overcome the earth's gravitational attraction. And to this we must add a bit more in order to propel the rocket to Mars.

Table II lists the minimum velocity that must be imparted to a rocket for it to reach the various planets:

TABLE II

PLANET	LAUNCH VELOCITY
Mercury	8.3 miles per second
Venus	7.2
Mars	7.2
Jupiter	8.7
Saturn	9.3
Uranus	9.6
Neptune	9.8
Pluto	10.0
"Escape"	10.2

In interpreting this table, we must remember that most of the required velocity is needed for escape from earth. This amounts to 6.95 miles per second, so if we subtract this from the launch velocities, we get the set of velocities in Table III (rounding off the escape velocity to seven miles per second).

These "required" velocities are actually those that would be necessary for a space probe floating in orbit about the sun. The reason for the plus and minus signs in Table III is that we must add velocity to go to the outer planets and we must subtract velocity to travel towards the sun. If we launch the space probe when the earth is at perihelion, and moving fastest in its orbit, we take advantage of this extra speed.

TABLE III

PLANET	REQUIRED VELOCITY
Mercury	−1.3 miles per second
Venus	−0.2
Mars	+0.2
Jupiter	+1.7
Saturn	+2.3
Uranus	+2.6
Neptune	+2.8
Pluto	+3.0
"Escape"	+3.2

To dispatch a space probe to Venus we must launch the vehicle "backward," that is, in a direction opposite to the earth's motion. This is the meaning of the minus sign in Table III. But no matter whether we fire in the direction of the earth's motion or in a direction opposed to it, we rely upon the earth's orbital velocity as the main propellant to speed the space probe on its way to the planets. Rocket experts merely manage to disengage the space probe from the earth's gravity and to aim it in the right direction with a small addition or subtraction of velocity. Then the sun takes over. The space probe moves from an earth orbit to another planetary orbit by proceeding along an elliptical path (the only closed or round-trip path allowed) which is governed by the sun. In other words, the space probe becomes an artificial planet moving in an eccentic orbit, the extremes of which come tangent to two planetary orbits.

Should a space probe be given a launch velocity of 10.2 miles per second (43 thousand miles per hour), it could escape from the sun's attraction. It would escape from the solar system and shoot off into space, proceeding on its course until caught by the gravitational field of another massive stellar object.

With this introduction to planetary travel, we need to consider some specifics of a trip to Mars. We must remember that earth and Mars move in their orbits at different speeds. The separation between the two planets is changing constantly, depending upon the orbital position of each planet. On September 7, 1956,

PROBES AND PLANETS   127

Mars made a close approach to earth—35,120,000 miles. The next such close approach occurs fifteen years later, but in between there are certain "most favorable" dates, as follows: November 16, 1962; December 23, 1964; January 26, 1967; and February 28, 1969. These are the best dates for attempting round-trip missions to Mars in a way that we shall describe in a moment. If one does not launch on the exact date, it is not disastrous, but there is a penalty that must be paid. Suppose, for example, that the launch velocity on the most favorable day is 7.2 miles per second. If one delays for a month, the required velocity becomes 7.4 miles per second. This is a stiff penalty for space experts and they would rather not pay it.

There are, of course, many times that one could shoot at Mars if one considers one-way trips and is willing to sacrifice payload weight by settling for very small space probes. But our concern is with round-trip missions that are most economical in rocket design, i.e., that yield a maximum payload. Analysis shows that the most economical flight pattern for high-thrust rockets of the Centaur and Saturn types is a semi-ellipse; that is, half an elliptical orbit, with the flight starting when the earth is at perihelion and traveling at its highest orbital speed. In Figure 10, solid lines show the orbits of earth and Mars, while the dotted curve represents the outward-bound path of the space probe. Note that the probe arrives at its orbital rendezvous with Mars at a point diametrically opposite its starting point and the sun is on a line joining the departure and arrival points.

The relative positions of earth and Mars are designated by the number 1 corresponding to launch time. After the space probe is launched and frees itself from the earth's gravitational attraction, it continues on its coast path as determined by its velocity and direction. The sun is, of course, the central force directing its pilgrimage to Mars. By the time that the probe reaches its rendezvous point with Mars, 259 days after launch, the earth has moved to position 2 and is over 100 million miles away. This fact obviously poses a severe communications problem.

If the space probe continued on in its elliptical orbit, then in another 259 days it would arrive at a point in the earth orbit corresponding to the launch point (position 1). But by this time, the earth would have lengthened its separation from the probe to 170 million miles. This would be very bad timing if the intent had been to meet up with earth again. A way out of this terrible problem of coming home from a Martian orbit is found by arranging a stopover on the trip. One cannot of course stand still in space, but one can hitch a ride with the planet Mars by "kicking" the space probe into a satellite orbit around it. Thus

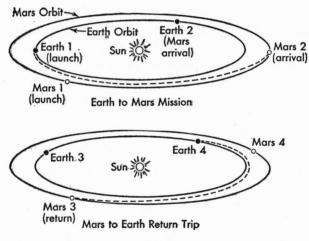

Fig. 10.

the space probe, providing the timing and thrust are correct, becomes an artificial moon circling Mars and participating in its orbital motion. The space probe proceeds along the Martian orbit, awaiting the command to return to earth when it is in the proper position.

Calculations show that the holdover on Mars—or rather in a Martian orbit—turns out to be 454 days. By now Mars has advanced to position 3 and leads the earth in orbit; this relationship is essential because the earth is the speedier of the two planets. Now the space probe is ejected from orbit and begins its return trip to earth, again a matter of 259 days. It arrives close to earth space 972 days after take-off. At this point it either telemeters its data to earth or effects re-entry.

Missions to Mars will acquire greater sophistication as greater thrust becomes available for interplanetary probes. Shorter round trips are also possible with the sacrifice of payload. The United States has a highly instrumented, Centaur-launched Mars probe slated for 1964. This will be followed by more massive probes as Saturn becomes operational and a one-ton space probe becomes feasible. A orbiter mission, if successful, will place the first artificial satellite or moon in orbit around Mars. There it will join two natural moons, two sisters named Phobos ("fear") and Deimos ("panic"). In this cheerful company the space probe might be christened Katastrophe.

Deimos, the smaller attendant of Mars, spins around it at a distance of 12,500 miles, while Phobos is an even closer companion, averaging a separation of 3,700 miles. About five miles in diameter, Deimos circles its planet once every 30 hours, whereas its sister makes a complete circuit in seven hours and 39 minutes. The artificial satellite might be sent into a one-day orbit. Once locked in the gravity grip of Mars, the space probe would be automatically oriented toward the Martian landscape.

Our knowledge about the surface of Mars is very skimpy and to a great extent inferential. An untrained observer, looking at Mars with a telescope of modest power, sees a reddish-orange orb without much in the way of surface detail. Some might glimpse dark areas near the equator and a whitish cap near the pole. Skilled observers, using large telescopes and enjoying good visibility conditions, can make out finer detail. They have noted, for example, that the white polar cap grows larger during the Martian winter and disappears in the summertime. Scientists conclude that this polar cap is formed by the freezing out of water vapor from the thin atmosphere, which has been found to consist of nitrogen, carbon dioxide plus some carbon monoxide, a few rare gases and a trace of water vapor.

No seas, lakes or rivers exist on Mars. Underneath a permanent bluish haze and occasionally shadowed by whitish-yellow clouds, the Martian surface is an arid expanse. Dust storms appear to sweep over the landscape but in spite of this mantle, changes in color and contrast appear, leading observers to believe that some form of vegetation exists and survives being coated with dust. Any plant life must be of a rudimentary form that had adapted itself to a lack of oxygen and violent changes in temperature. The noonday Martian sun warms up equatorial zones to a comfortable 85° F. but at night the absence of a protecting atmosphere drops the temperature far below zero.

Close-up photography of Mars may give some clues to the nature of the vegetation, but identification of the plant forms must await contact with the Martian soil. Just as it is much more difficult to land on and take off from the moon than to accomplish a circumlunar mission, so, too, it is a much greater undertaking to descend to and return from the Martian surface. A one-way expedition would be vastly easier but then one is faced with the problem of relaying the acquired data over interplanetary distances. A compromise, and more complicated, possibility is to eject a capsule from the space probe, impact it upon Mars, and relay the data back to the space probe where it can be stored for retransmittal to earth.

Scientists wish to acquire a great deal of data about Mars and its environment. For example, they want to measure the Martian magnetic field and to determine if Van Allen radiation belts encircle Mars. They wish to learn as much as possible about the Martian atmosphere, about surface temperatures, the presence of water on the surface, and many other details. Yet the planetary probe which is projectible by the U.S. Centaur rocket can carry only a few hundred pounds of scientific instruments. An improved version of a spacecraft would weigh 800 pounds and be operational in 1964. Such a space vehicle would be dispatched on "near-miss" missions and could not be guided into an orbit around Mars. Sometime in 1966 or 1967 a Mars space probe, launched by Saturn, could carry a payload of several thousand pounds. This could be thrust into a Martian orbit and could carry entry capsules for exploration of the Martian atmosphere.

The capsule would relay its observations to the spacecraft, circling Mars at an altitude of about 1,000 miles, which would relay coded data back to earth. A more sophisticated flight mission to Mars would carry guidance and propulsion equipment able to leave the Martian orbit and return to earth. Barring radical breakthroughs in communication techniques, return-to-earth missions appear to be most feasible for reception of photographic records of good quality.

The United States has established three powerful stations for communicating with probes sent on deep-space missions. One station, equipped with an 85-foot parabolic antenna and ultrasensitive radio receivers, is located at Goldstone, California, in a desert about 100 miles from Los Angeles. Another has been constructed at Woomera in Australia and a third near Johannesburg, South Africa. The location of the three stations allows at least one of them to "look at" a space probe regardless of its position in space.

Let us consider the communication between a Martian space probe and an earth station of the Goldstone type. The steps in the communication process are: acquisition of the data by sensitive instruments; in-put of these data (modulation) to a transmitter; feed-in of the transmitter's power to an antenna; radiation of this information to the earth station; reception of the signal; amplification of the signal; recording and analysis of the data. Clearly, there are many links in this chain of communication. Scientists and communications engineers have made huge strides in developing the over-all chain, but the problem of communicating over interplanetary distances is very severe. It becomes even worse if we consider the transmission of a voice signal or a television picture.

Most space devices in the first years of the space age used omnidirectional radio transmitters; that is, signals were broadcast in all directions. This is an extremely wasteful process since a receiver at a distance intercepts only a tiny fraction of the transmitted energy. It is more sophisticated communication procedure to beam the information in one direction so that the energy is concentrated; however, it must be directed properly, otherwise it would be a futile operation.

Transmission of a television picture across millions of miles of space requires more than a million times the power needed to send a simple radio signal. Commenting on this fact, NASA communications expert Leonard Jaffe explained:

One of the most interesting things that we can do if we are to approach the planets with our space vehicles is to take a picture of the surface of the planet. If we take a look at the amount of power required to send a television picture back from a planet, such as Mars, we would end up with a figure of 10 billion watts, a formidable amount of power.

This is not only a formidable amount of power, it is fantastic to assume that it could be packaged in a space vehicle. It is many times the total power capacity of the plants supplying electricity to New York City.

Since there are many links in the Mars-to-earth communication sequence, there are also many possibilities for improving the performance of the system. Slowing down the transmission rate of the TV picture, perfecting better receivers and establishing an earth-satellite "big dish" antenna—these possibilities point to sharp reductions in the power requirements, but even with the best gains very considerable amounts of on-board electrical power will be required. Here the development of nuclear-electric plants offers the potential of lightweight power for space vehicles.

Considering the power demands for interplanetary transmission of a television picture, it is possible that our first picture of Mars will be received from a round-trip mission that either returns to earth or relays a picture as it passes through earth-space. The first photograph of Mars is bound to be a sensation on earth.

Mars may be inhospitable but at least it is gracious enough to expose its surface to view. Our sister planet, Venus, is perpetually shrouded in a thick veil of yellowish clouds and we can only speculate about what lies below the sea of mist. We do not even know how long the day is on Venus since no point on its surface can be observed in rotation. Viewed through a telescope, Venus appears to be a brilliant blank disk; observations of changes in the cloud cover have been reported, but no reliable conclusions can be drawn about the surface. Infrared measurements show that the temperature above the clouds is about 100° F. and recent radio studies indicate that below-cloud temperatures run up to 570° F. Should the surface of Venus approach such temperatures, then no water can exist there. We are led to conclude that Venus is probably an arid, gloomy, planet, swept by dust storms.

In many respects Venus is the twin of earth. Its physical size and its gravity are not too dissimilar to our own. The physical likeness, plus its proximity to earth, have stimulated people in the past to conjure up what we now regard as fallacious views of Venus. Anyone who looks back into the literature will discover references to Venus' being covered with verdant jungles, akin to those which abounded on earth during the era when coal beds were being formed. This view is now unpopular for a good scientific reason: If such jungles existed, growing plants would have converted the atmosphere into one rich in oxygen. Yet no detectable amounts of oxygen have been observed on Venus. The atmosphere appears to be largely carbon dioxide with some possible amounts of water vapor and nitrogen. The thick blanket of carbon dioxide serves as an insulator and probably keeps the surface temperature of Venus above the boiling point of water. It is estimated that the atmosphere of Venus is such that it exerts a surface pressure twice as great as our earth sea-level pressure.

Although Venus keeps its face hidden under an unrelenting overcast, and our information is rather meager about conditions on the planet, space experts are understandably not optimistic about finding life there. The atmosphere is simply too forbidding to hold out much hope that Venus is more hospitable to life than Mars. This fact, however, does not deter space enthusiasts from wanting to explore Venusian space and send entry capsules into the great cloud masses surrounding the planet.

Pioneer V or 1960 Alpha, the first U.S. space flight of 1960, was launched on March 11, 1960. Its mission: to investigate interplanetary space between the orbits of earth and Venus and

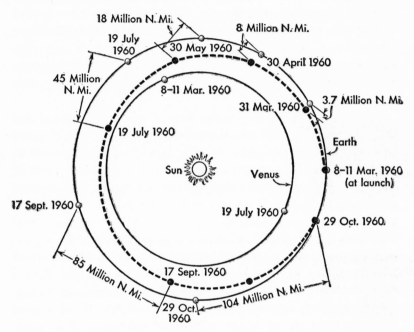

Fig. 11. The trajectory of Pioneer V, a space probe sent between the 50 orbits of Earth and Venus. *NASA*

to test space-probe-to-earth communications at extreme range. At burn-out of the third stage, the payload—a 26-inch sphere with four paddle wheels covered with 4800 solar cells—achieved a speed of 24,689 miles per hour. The 95-pound Pioneer V carried 40 pounds of instruments on its historic flight to the vicinity of Venus. The orbit of Pioneer V is shown in Fig. 11 where the relative separation of earth and the space probe can be appreciated for various times after launch.

There were twin radio transmitters aboard Pioneer V, one a five-watt and the other a 150-watt unit. On June 26, 1960, the last message from Pioneer V was received by the Jodrell Bank radiotelescope in Britain. At this time the earth-probe distance was 22.5 million miles. The faint signal sent through space on ultra-high frequency (378 megacycles per second) was picked up by the 250-ft. antenna dish at Jodrell Bank. Pioneer V is now a "dead" or "dark" object orbiting the sun with a perihelion of 74.9 million miles and an aphelion of 92.3 million miles. It takes 311.6 days to complete its 506-million-mile trip around the sun.

Pioneer V was an exploratory probe without sufficient accuracy (and no mid-course or terminal guidance) to come very close to Venus. For such a probe the control of the velocity at cut-off is very important; an error of ten miles per hour means a miss of over half a million miles in orbit. Just as in the case of the rocket to Mars, a mission to Venus has certain most favorable days for take-off. These occur about every two years—August 16, 1962; March 28, 1964; October 27, 1965; June 5, 1967; January 11, 1969. Transit times to Venus are less than to Mars because of the shorter distances to be traveled.

Space probes to Mars and Venus rate the highest priority among scientists who wish to explore the solar system. Mars ranks highest among the planets in terms of its qualifications for sustaining some form, however primitive, of life. Naturally, scientists are interested in the giant planets, but their accessibility is restricted to the more distant future. But in the solar system the sun outranks all the other bodies as the object of interest. Someday, specially equipped probes will be sent inside Mercury's orbit to take a closer look at the sun; meanwhile, earth observations, and our recently acquired knowledge of nuclear physics, permit us to understand much about the sun.

11

THE SUN AND THE STARS

INTERPLANETARY flights are rigorously controlled by the gravitational power of the sun, which reaches out over vast distances and prescribes the motion of all objects within the solar system. The sun holds sway over its planetary family because of the immenseness of its mass. It is 332 thousand times heavier than earth and 743 times heavier than its entire family of nine planets.

The sun is more than a massive center of gravity for the solar system. It is an enormous heat engine which is exquisitely balanced for the orderly release of elemental energy. By studying the sun we can understand more about other stars more remote from us.

Recent advances in science permit us to understand the nature of the sun's inner workings and even allow us to theorize with some confidence about the sun's origin and its planetary family. We know that the ultimate stuff composing our earth and the planets consists of the same chemical elements as make up our central sun. To be sure, there is more hydrogen and less oxygen in our sun than on our planet, but the fundamental building blocks—the tiniest constituents—all belong to the same family of elements. Thus we do not need to resort to the unknown or supernatural in order to inquire into the order of our solar system.

Was the sun always as big, always as bright as it is today? How long has it been shining and where does it gain its seemingly inexhaustible energy? What is its origin? What is its ultimate destiny?

These are surely profound and tantalizing questions and it is a tribute to man that he even asks them with hope of answer. Only a relatively few years ago, our state of knowledge was such that the "answers" were highly speculative. They could not be based upon solid ground until scientists explored a most unlikely realm—the inner atom. To understand the workings of the sun, millions of miles away, and of the stars even more remote, scientists probed into the dark domain of the atom's core.

Distances inside the atom are infinitesimally minute. By way of illustration, if we take a foot as the unit of comparison, it is about a trillion feet across the earth's orbit, whereas the core of the largest atom measures less than one trillionth of a foot. The reason physicists looked to the atom as a font of knowledge was quite straightforward; they knew that the whole is the sum of its parts and if one wished to understand the sun, it was essential to analyze the behavior of its smallest parts.

The study of the inner atom proceeded at a rather jerky pace throughout the first three decades of this century, not because of a lack of brainpower but because the physicist needed sharper tools to ply his craft. Man's fingers were too blunt an instrument to explore the crevasses of the atom; he needed special devices to probe the microcosm. These were slow in coming, but gradually the tools emerged. The exquisitely sensitive Geiger counter, the elegant Wilson cloud chamber which made visible the track of atomic particles, and improvements in electronic instruments gave the physicist means to study the atom. But he needed even more; he required some weapons of attack. By the mid-thirties, as the Great Depression gripped the nation and slowed its tempo, the pace of nuclear science quickened. The development of high-energy machines like the cyclotron allowed nuclear physicists to bombard the atom.

The citadel of the atom crumbled under attack. Initial breachings of the ramparts revealed certain secrets that were to have a calamitous impact upon society when they made possible the development of the A-bomb. But they also gave a Cornell University professor some vital clues to the solution of a problem that had intrigued him for a number of years. Dr. Hans A. Bethe seized upon the data emanating from the nuclear-physics laboratories and applied the new information to an old problem —the origin of the sun's heat.

Dr. Bethe started with two well-established pieces of information. First, that the sun's core soared to a temperature of almost 30 million degrees Fahrenheit. Second, that the innermost part of the sun contained vast quantities of hydrogen subjected to superpressure by the great outer mantle of hot gas. He knew that heat emerged from this solar furnace at a definite rate, measured by astrophysicists as equal to one-third trillion trillion kilowatts. This amount of power was required to account for the heat striking the earth's surface.

Laboratory data showed that two hydrogen atoms, colliding with each other at high speed, could fuse together. The synthesis of four hydrogen atoms formed one atom of helium, the next-heaviest element in the periodic scheme of elements. In the conversion of hydrogen into helium, each hydrogen atom gave up a small part of its mass. The result was that the mass of the four hydrogen atoms, before fusion, was slightly more than after synthesis into a single helium atom. In effect some atomic mass was "lost" in the fusion process. Einstein's Special Theory of

THE SUN AND THE STARS 139

Relativity established the now-famous mass-energy relation E equals mc². E stands for energy, m for mass, and c is the symbol for the velocity of light—a constant which enters into the mathematical formula. According to this Einstein relationship, a very small amount of matter is equivalent to a great deal of energy. For example, the matter in an ordinary aspirin tablet would, if wholly converted into energy, equal the force of almost 20 million pounds of TNT.

Dr. Bethe calculated that deep inside the sun's fiery core, the hydrogen atoms should be in constant collision and even though they moved with speeds far less than those achieved in cyclotrons, some of them would fuse together to form helium. This process is technically known as a thermonuclear reaction or, more picturesquely, as nuclear burning. Details of his theory are too complex to discuss here; the important thing is that Dr. Bethe's calculations showed that hydrogen burning to form helium satisfactorily accounted for the sun's vast outpouring of energy.

That the solar heat machine operates on a prodigious scale of hydrogen stoking can be appreciated if we consider that 600 million tons of hydrogen are burned every second. At this rate of fuel consumption it might seem that the sun would soon burn out and dim the light of the solar system. However, the hydrogen reservoir in the sun assures a fuel supply adequate for many billions of years, assuming that the sun keeps running at the same power. Naturally, the sun continually loses weight owing to the Einstein-mass which is lost as heat energy; this amounts to 300 billion tons every day—such a drop in the bucket, compared to the sun's total mass, that it is not important. As long as we are in the realm of staggering statistics, I might mention that the energy output of all the stars in our galaxy, the Milky Way, is over 100 billion times more than that of our sun. And in the known universe, including all the galaxies, we have an outpouring of energy another 100 billion times that of our galaxy.

Modern science provides a neat explanation for the present heat output of our sun, but what about the past? How was the sun's interior heated to a point where it could start up its hydrogen burning? To answer such questions, we need to go beyond the bounds of the laboratory and enter into the somewhat rarified atmosphere of speculation. We are asking, in effect, that the scientist spin back the clock of time and tell what happened at the beginning. He obviously does not know—especially if by "beginning" you mean the instant of genesis—but he has some fascinating theories to account for the origin of our solar system.

Scientists now believe that our sun and its planetary family were once a vast veil of diffuse, rather cold, gas—a darkness in the galaxy. Given this immense primordial gas, certain patterns of behavior for the particles of matter can be defined. Bear in mind that this "gas" was exceedingly tenuous—so dilute, in fact, that it contained far fewer bits of matter than the most perfect vacuum that man has ever achieved. This far-stretching gas cloud had its own motion—a slow rotary movement of the whole, interwoven with streaming, internal turmoil. This was the bleak, vacuous state of our solar system over five billion years ago. Not a promising beginning for the spectacle we see around us.

Given such dilute, cool gas, scientists agree that gravitational forces should cause much of the gas to condense toward a central core. The inwardly spiraling streams of gas should lead to an agglomeration of globs of matter moving with ever-faster rotatory motion. The effect was to produce a spinning central body of matter which gradually became warmer and then hot enough to be luminous as the compressive force of the coalescing gas raised the temperature of the central core. At the same time the accumulating outer mantle of the primitive sun formed an insulating mantle, trapping the inner heat and thus raising the temperature of the core. Soon the great mass of the proto-sun began to glow with its trapped self-heat. Out of the darkness, there came light, dull red at first and then brighter as the proto-sun grew in size and in temperature. What kind of scene did this first solar light illuminate? Scholars agree on the origin of the sun in this way, but they are of several minds about the origin of the planetary family. They concur that the planets were formed by condensation of gaseous matter, but some believe this may have preceded the formation of the sun, while others think that the planets were formed after the sun, spinning off an equatorial rim or condensing from a nebular web.

To return to the sun, the presence of large quantities of hydrogen in the hot, central core set the stage for Act One of the thermonuclear drama. The solar furnace was primed for ignition. Ever so gradually, the random collision of extra-speedy hydrogen atoms produced fusion and the release of energy. This, in turn, elevated the core temperature and the atoms of hydrogen gained a bit more speed. (The fusion reaction of hydrogen depends very sensitively upon the speed or "temperature" of the hydrogen atoms; the higher the speed, the more readily fusion occurs.) Endlessly, the process repeated itself until finally the sun achieved its present temperature. A neat balance was struck between the tendency of the temperature to rise higher and the size of the sun, which, by swelling under pressure of greater central heat, assumed a new size and capacity to radiate heat from its surface. Cooling and core contraction were offset by shrinkage of the outer mantle of the sun and consequent compressive heating. Thus the sun proved to be self-regulating, having a built-in thermostat for maintaining its temperature. That is why the planetary system has been basking in the same solar heat for the past five billion years.

The sun is a concentrated point of heat-light warming the planets and sustaining life on earth and perhaps some form of life on Mars. Venus remains a question mark since there is no way to peer underneath its blanket of perpetual clouds. Earth and its two neighbors orbit the sun in a zone where the heat is neither too great nor too little for life to flourish. Mercury, as we have noted, keeps one face permanently fixed on the sun, and the intense sunshine keeps that side above the temperature of melting lead. As one goes beyond Mars, the sunshine weakens for the same reason that light gets dimmer when you walk away from a light bulb in a large room. We say that the intensity of the light (and heat) falls off as the inverse square of the distance from the light source. Doubling the distance reduces the light intensity to one fourth. This rapid drop-off of light results in a chilly climate for the outer planets and dictates against the existence of life on them.

The fact that there exists a "life zone" or a band of hospitable orbit limits for planets is of considerable importance, especially when we consider that planetary systems are quite common throughout our galaxy and throughout the universe. It means that for every star which resembles our sun (this qualification has to be made since there are many stars with histories quite unlike that of our sun) there is a zone within which one might expect life of some kind to flourish if the planet provides a suitable environment. Sufficient, but not too much, heat is a prime essential for the life process.

Any planet that qualifies as an abode for living organisms needs to describe fairly circular paths around the central star. Too eccentric an orbit would subject the planet to temperature extremes and thus prejudice the generation and viability of living things.

We thus have two conditions which planetary orbits must fulfill in order to be hospitable to life. They must lie in a temperate heat zone and they must be fairly circular. In the next chapter we will add more qualifications regarding the planet's environment; here, we consider one more feature—the character of the host, the central star which sponsors life on the planet.

The stellar flame that provides the heat and light so essential to the origin and evolution of living organisms has to be both steady and enduring. Irregularities in the heat-light output could terminate even rudimentary life forms abruptly. One has only to think of an ice cap enveloping the planet or a searing heat wave drying up the land. Observations of the many stars, whose heat output can be measured quite readily by sensitive instruments attached to giant telescopes, show that only occasionally do stars misbehave. The great majority lead well-adjusted lives, marked by a steady output of energy.

In looking at the stars and measuring their light, we must remember that we are on the receiving end of light which was emitted sometime in the past. We see the stars as they were, not as they are. The astronomer peers into the past when he studies the light from distant stars. He measures the distance to the stars with a unit called the light-year. This is the distance traveled by a ray of light in one year. Since the velocity of light is 186,000 miles per second, the light-year is equal to a distance of about six trillion miles. Huge telescopes such as the 200-inch instrument on Mt. Palomar have the ability to focus light from the remotest stars. Careful studies have revealed the existence of stars several billion light-years away from us. In other words these stars are 12 billion trillion miles away.

As astronomers turn their telescopes upon the stars, they can classify them in various categories. The two principal characteristics used in this stellar classification are the luminosity, or brightness, and the star color, or temperature. Sorted out in this way, the stars group themselves into a regular sequence (with some exceptions) running from weakly luminous, cool stars to brilliant hot stars. Our sun lies midway between these extremes. The big, hot stars are fast-burners and they blaze their way through their hydrogen fuel supply as a prodigal sun. Their life story—their time of fiery glory—ends in a hundred million years. Others run through their hydrogen inheritance in a billion years. Whatever forms of life they might generate on suitably disposed planetary offspring in this brief (measured on an evolutionary time scale) span of time would be doomed by the catastrophic expansion of the star's transformation to a giant, red star. This is the ultimate fate of our sun.

Stars with very long lives—the slow-burners which endure for a hundred billion years or more—have a low heat output. They warm up only a very limited planetary zone. Middle-class stars like our sun burn hydrogen on a modest scale, producing medium heat over ten billion years or so. In our own galaxy there are perhaps five billion stars which can be classed with our sun. We eliminate from our census all but single stars since double and triple stars are not apt to have planets circulating in stable orbits, favorable for life.

We must add yet another requirement which is not exclusively confined to the parent star but may apply to nearby stars as well. The host star should not shower its planetary family with excessive quantities of penetrating radiation. In the case of our planet earth we are bombarded by a hail of penetrating rays called "cosmic rays." Most of the rays which penetrate down to the earth's surface come from outer space and their origin is still a matter of controversy among scientists. Some of the rays striking the earth's outer mantle come from our sun. We know that the primary rays, that is, those striking the top of our atmosphere, are largely fast-moving hydrogen nuclei (i.e., atoms minus their outer electrons). Some helium nuclei also rain down upon our planet together with about one per cent of heavier nuclei. These energetic particles rarely reach sea level; they smash into atoms of nitrogen and oxygen in the upper air and release a spray of atomic particles which cascade down to earth. A few of the rays are so powerful that they penetrate into the earth; for example, they have been measured inside deep lead mines.

This penetrating radiation, reinforced by rays emitted by radioactive minerals in the earth's crust, bombards human beings throughout their lives. It forms a natural background to which everyone is exposed and has been exposed throughout the history of the planet. The human race has evolved under this incessant drizzle of radiation. In fact, the penetrating rays produce genetic mutation or hereditary changes a small percentage of which are beneficial to the species, providing one accepts the cruel penalty of the much more abundant harmful mutations. But there is a great difference between a drizzle and a downpour and the effects of severe irradiation would prejudice the evolution of life forms.

Our sun sometimes flares up and sends a flood of penetrating radiation surging through space. This feature of the solar temperament has been discovered recently and we still need to learn more about the phenomenon. It is not a terrestrial hazard, but for planets less protected by a thick atmosphere, it might be significant. It might serve to disqualify some stars as candidates for the fostering of life.

We have narrowed down the list of stars which could provide their planetary families with the proper environment for life. But so far we have not touched upon the key question: How many stars have planetary offspring?

It is a curious fact that up until quite recently almost all the experts were very pessimistic about the occurrence of planets around stars. In part this is explained by the popularity of the collision theory of the origin of our solar system. It was thought that a star collided with our sun—not actual impact but a close approach—and great chunks of matter were thrown out to become planets. Such a stellar collision would be an extremely rare occurrence. Perhaps this is what made the theory so appealing to many; it made a very special place in the universe for our solar system. Since star-star impacts would be most frequent, one would expect to find very few planets in our galaxy or, for that matter, in other galaxies. More acceptable theories, which replaced the collision theory, view the creation of planets as more normal than abnormal.

As the famous astronomer Dr. Otto Struve puts it: "It is safe to say, in fact, that billions of stars in our Milky Way possess families of planets. Evidence seems to be overwhelmingly in favor of the conclusion that all, or most, solar-type stars possess planetary systems resembling our own."

Dr. Struve's words no longer produce a shock effect in the scientific community. But to the average man, Dr. Struve's opinion seems close to heresy. After all, if one grants that there may be billions of planetary systems in our galaxy—not to mention vastly more planets in other galaxies—a logical but to many a deeply disturbing question arises: "Is there life on other planets?"

Are there other earths spinning around their own suns in the depths of space? Those who have cherished the notion that life on earth is unique find the question vexing and worrisome. I suspect that only a few people are disturbed at present, but I believe that as awareness of the implications of the question becomes more general, the possibility of extraterrestrial life will be the subject of profound debate.

12

LIFE IN THE UNIVERSE

EVEN THE most powerful telescope on earth cannot reveal directly the presence of planets circling other stars. To put the matter in hypothetical reverse, if an astronomer could transport the Mt. Palomar telescope to the nearest star, Alpha Centauri, and look at our solar system, he would never see the earth. It would be lost in the bright glare of the sun. Alpha Centauri is only 4.3 light-years from us, a mere 26 million million miles, and the bulk of the stars in the Milky Way are thousands of light years away from us.

Despite our inability to observe other planets in motion about central stars, we can learn much about these stars and deduce something about the habitability of their assumed planets. In the last chapter we defined the zones of hospitality around host stars and we came to the conclusion that there must be literally billions of stars with planetary families suitable for the fostering of life. So far we have avoided defining "life," and this circumvention ends at this point.

148

I wish to make a fundamental point before plunging into the question of life. It is that the universe is everywhere composed of the same fundamental elements. The light from the nearest and the most remote stars tells us that without exception they are composed of elements with which we are familiar here on earth. The family of elements ranges from hydrogen to uranium and includes ninety-two members. Each element, when brought to an incandescent state, as in a star or in an electrical discharge in the laboratory, emits colored light which is distinctive. An instrument known as the spectroscope, a combination of glass prisms and lenses, permits one to analyze the light emitted by a substance. The spectroscope shreds the light into fine components so that a scientist can determine what elements compose the incandescent light source.

Invariably when astronomers photograph the stars, whether near or far, the spectra, or patterns of light, reveal the same elements found on earth. To be sure, the composition of the stars may be quite different, some containing mostly hydrogen, and others exhibiting a mixture of elements—helium, calcium, carbon, iron and nickel. We are certainly justified in assuming that planets circulating around these stars are composed of the same elements as the stars, although the percentage composition may vary widely. Whatever forms of life may exist on these planets, they must be built up out of the atoms known to us on earth. We need seek no mystical form of life as something utterly different in kind from what we conceive of with our mortal brains.

In essence, then, the telescope and spectroscope tell us that the universe is based upon a common fundamental substructure. Any extraterrestrial forms of life will therefore be of a chemical nature, that is, formed of the various elements in their atomic and molecular patterns. This rules out life under conditions where chemical forms or aggregates of molecules are impossible —as for example, inside or even near hot stars. Molecules do not stay stuck together at the high temperatures found in stars. In fact, even atoms break down and lose their outer electrons.

Chemists understand very well how atoms stick together to

form molecules. They have studied carefully the nature of the chemical bond uniting parts of the molecule and they know the temperatures at which these bonds break. Thus we can set an upper liimit for the temperature at which molecules no longer stay together and this would prescribe the temperature conditions necessary for a planet to foster life. If we made no attempt to distinguish between various kinds of molecules, such as organic benzene and inorganic tungsten carbide, the temperature limit would not be too meaningful. Metallic compounds can have high melting points whereas organic or carbon-containing compounds decompose at relatively low temperatures. We need to ask which atoms seem to be most critical for the formation of living organisms.

Life on the planet earth is carbon-based. Carbon is without peer as an atom-hub for the building of complex molecules. A vast variety of chemical compounds—known as organic compounds—totaling almost half a million types, are possible when carbon atoms are linked to atoms of other elements. Hydrogen and oxygen atoms join up with carbon atoms very easily and form a class of compounds known as hydrocarbons. All in all, it is no exaggeration to call carbon the "architectural atom."

Life, as we know it, is organic in nature. This fact allows us to stipulate a temperature limit. Dr. Harold C. Urey, the noted chemist, defined the limit. "On the basis of our knowledge of the behavior of carbon compounds," he said, "it seems reasonable to say definitely that no life of the kind we see on earth, or any approximation to it, could exist at 250° C. or above."

Carbon-based life and an aqueous environment go hand in hand. The microbe and man share a common chemical base— water and hydrocarbons. An organism containing water could not undergo biological evolution in an environment far below the freezing point of water. A few organisms—certain bacteria and algae—manage to survive under unusual temperatures. For example, some thermophylic bacteria resist high temperature and some even survive in sulphurous hot springs but these exceptions still conform to Dr. Urey's stipulation of the upper temperature limit.

Biologists concede that non-water-dependent organisms could evolve and it is possible to conceive of noncarbonaceous compounds as the basis for life. Silicon—the common ingredient in ordinary sand—might substitute for carbon as an atom-hub. But these "exotic" forms of life need not concern us; it is sufficient to explore the possibilities for carbon-based organisms.

The vast array of carbon compounds which can be assembled from a relatively small number of component elements—carbon, oxygen, hydrogen, phosphorus and sulphur—introduces and facilitates the factor of complexity in organization and function of organisms. Whether we deal with a bacterium, a mosquito or a monkey, we meet up with single cells of comparable complexity. Geneticist Joshua Lederberg has pointed to a deeper common bond in terrestrial life. "Our plants, animals and bacteria," he observed, "share a remarkable list of biochemical components, and a biochemist cannot easily distinguish extracts of yeast cells and beef muscle. Among these components, the nucleic acids warrant first attention. Although they constitute the hereditary material, so that all the variety of terrestrial life can be referred to subtle differences in the nucleic acids, the same basic structure is found in the nuclei of all cells."

Dr. Lederberg's observation cuts deeply into the issue of "life." His analysis goes beyond the universal kinship of terrestrial life which Charles Darwin recognized so astutely. It penetrates inside the living cell and inquires as to the ultimate common denominator of life. Many single cells undergo mitosis —they divide, thus exhibiting growth and implying energy comsumption—and the microscope reveals a complicated yet orderly rearrangement of cellular constituents. There is design and direction and traffic control within the single cell. And this follows a universal pattern. As Dr. Lederberg points out, the pattern goes deep—far beyond what the microscope reveals to what the biochemist finds. It points to nucleic acid as the ultimate organizer of cellular activity.

Charles Darwin was unaware of nucleic acid (it had not been discovered) in 1871 when he wrote in a letter:

It is often said that all the conditions for the first production of a living organism are now present, which could ever have been present. But if (and oh! what a big if) we could conceive in some warm little pond, with all sorts of ammonia and phosphoric salts, light, heat, electricity, &c present, that a proteine compound was chemically formed ready to undergo still more complex changes . . .

Darwin's warm little pond filled with chemicals and exposed to energy sources such as light and electricity turned out to be an amazing anticipation of experiments performed in the past decade.

Whereas Darwin sought the answer to the mystery of life's origin in an earthly site, others invoked an extraterrestrial, indeed, a cosmic source of life. The famous physical chemist Svante Arrhenius developed a theory of panspermia; which holds that life is distributed throughout cosmic space. The Swedish Nobel Prize winner theorized that the earth was colonized by tiny microorganisms—spores—which drifted through space and landed on earth where they flourished. Arrhenius' theory had some very real difficulties. For example, how did the spores get injected into space, how did they withstand the assault by ultraviolet rays, how did they survive years, even millennia, of wandering in the vacuum of space exposed to ultra-low temperatures? Despite the technical stumbling blocks, some of which seem less fearsome today, the theory of panspermia fascinated many people. It is undergoing something of a revival today as the possibility of reaching the moon draws closer. Perhaps somewhere on or below the surface of the moon an experimental answer can be given to resolve the controversy over the interplanetary innoculation of life through the agency of drifting spores.

Some evidence bearing on the panspermia theory might be found in analysis of those meteorites which survive their fiery descent through the earth's atmosphere. Pasteur is reported to have examined specimens of meteorites for traces of micro-organisms, but he obtained negative results. Dr. C. P. Lipman studied a number of meteorites, sterilizing their surfaces to exclude earth bacteria and then transferring bits of internal fragments to a nutrient medium. In 1932 he announced that rodlike and spheroid (cocci) bacteria grew from the culture. The bacteria were apparently identical with species found on earth. The possibility (to many, the probability) that the experimental technique did not quarantine native (home-grown) bacteria left the results in doubt.

Dr. Melvin Calvin, University of California chemist, carefully examined a small piece of a meteorite which fell on Kentucky soil in 1950. The California researcher looked, not for bacteria which would spring to life, but for dead remnants—complex, ancestral molecules—essential links in the chain of life. Professor Calvin reported finding "very reasonable evidence of the presence of molecules of the aromatic heterocyclic type resembling the pyrimidines and purines present in terrestrial genetic material." The molecules specified are fragments of more complex molecules present in the chromosomes. "The samples indicate," concluded Dr. Calvin, "that the same evolutionary processes that unfolded on earth have gone on somewhere else."

Research on meteorite samples needs to be extended but the initial results of work going at the University of California are intriguing. There are, however, additional lines of investigation which are just as provocative and even more revealing. They go back some thirty years to the research of the British biologist J. B. S. Haldane and the Russian biochemist Alexander I. Oparin. Both sought to understand the phenomenon of biopoesis, the process whereby life evolves from inorganic origins. Theories about the origin of life on this planet begin by assuming that the earth was originally very elemental—sea, land and air. The oceans were much as they are today but the continents were devoid of any vegetation and the primitive atmosphere probably contained some hydrogen, methane, ammonia, water vapor and nitrogen. Oxygen, so important to life, was probably not present in significant quantities as a free gas. These constituted the basic chemical ingredients for the building of complex, organic compounds.

The primordial earth was subjected to an inflow of energy comprising such forms as sunlight, cosmic rays, and electrical discharges from lightning. The earth's surface was at the time completely sterile. As Professor Oparin points out in his classic book *The Origin of Life on Earth,* the initial sterility of the earth is very significant for the survival of the first life form. No enemies were present to devour the first bit of life that might flourish.

Oparin advanced the theory that life originated, billions of years ago, in this primitive environment. He conceived of the ocean as a kind of thin organic soup—an accumulation of organic compounds synthesized in the atmosphere. Professor Oparin published his ideas in 1935 but it was not until the early 1950's that experimental proof of the first link in the life chain could be found.

Research conducted at the University of Chicago aimed at duplicating inside a test tube events which might have taken place billions of years ago in the earth's primitive atmosphere. Dr. Stanley L. Miller, working in the laboratory of Professor Harold C. Urey, used a closed glass system, consisting of a pint flask of water and a gallon flask containing an atmosphere of methane, ammonia and hydrogen. The water was kept boiling so that water vapor saturated the gaseous mixture in the gallon flask. An electric spark was flashed repeatedly across electrodes fused into the glass so that miniature lightning resounded through the mixture of gases. The apparatus was kept running for a full week.

When Dr. Miller stopped the experiment and made a chemical analysis of the gases inside the apparatus, he got some surprising results. He was able to identify complex hydrocarbons such as glycine, formic acid, acetic acid and urea. The simple experiment proved that fairly complex hydrocarbon compounds could be synthesized from simple gases through the addition of electrical energy to the gaseous atmosphere. Dr. Miller knew that glycine was the simplest of the amino acids, which are fundamental chemical entities in living tissue. The experiment marked a beginning of an exciting new experimental approach to the origin of life, but it was of course a chemical synthesis, not a biological one. It served to illuminate how organic compounds might have been formed in prebiological times.

Dr. Philip Abelson, an atomic scientist with a broad range of interests, including biology and geophysics, extended the Chicago experiments at his Carnegie Institution laboratory in Washington, D.C. Using a variety of different gaseous atmospheres, he identified a score of complex organic compounds produced by irradiating the gaseous mixtures. I recall visiting his laboratory one morning when he uncorked an "atmospheric flask" which had been cooking overnight. "Smell it," he invited, extending the opened flask to me. My nose detected the distinctive aromatic smell of the amino acids which had been synthesized in the experiment.

The overnight irradiation of a simulated, primitive atmosphere with a constant barrage of electrical energy must be viewed as a compression in time of events which might have taken countless years. No one can say how long nature took to duplicate the synthesis in the test-tube experiment. Probably strong ultraviolet light served as the energy source in nature, rather than lightning. Time, however, was not of the essence; a hundred million years was relatively unimportant on a billion-year scale. Nature could afford to be patient.

The gradual synthesis of complex chemical compounds and their uptake in the ocean created what could be regarded as a vast oceanic seedbed, awaiting the quickening touch of the chance encounter of complex molecules which might be regarded as the infinitesimal spark of life. On a molecular scale, a definition of life is elusive, but self-duplication, or replication, of a giant molecule would be a vital first step on the road to life.

Somewhere in the recesses of time the chance conjunction of

molecules or the random alteration of a large, inert molecule bequeathed to it an ability to replicate. This emergence of an active molecule, capable of duplicating itself, was a monumental step up the evolutionary ladder. Self-duplication is a characteristic of all living systems, so it is no exaggeration to describe the first replicating molecule as "living." Such a characterization is a far cry from the layman's notion of living and dead, but on a molecular scale the usual concepts of what is living need to be refashioned.

Perhaps the first "living" molecule was a simple nucleic acid which, through a combination of favorable circumstances in its local environment, was able to propagate itself. The absence of biological enemies was naturally of great protective value to the viability of the replicating molecule. Now we shall not attempt to pretend that scientists know the linkage between the events tracing from the origin of the replicating molecule to man. There is a vast chasm in our knowledge of the chain of events, but it is possible to theorize about the evolutionary steps.

Dr. George W. Beadle, distinguished geneticist at the California Institute of Technology, summed up the new perspective of man and the molecule:

It is now possible to conceive how elements, inorganic molecules, organic molecules, primitive virus-like living systems, cellular organisms, and finally man, might have evolved step-wise from a primitive universe of hydrogen—with no single step more difficult to understand than the atomic nuclear reactions, chemical processes and genetic mutations we observe and investigate experimentally today.

One reason why Dr. Beadle can make such a statement is that modern science has uncovered much new information about the mechanism of replication in molecular systems. The British scientist F.H.C. Crick and the American biologist J.D. Watson, working at Cambridge University, get credit for making a most valuable contribution to our knowledge of replication. In 1952 they explored the structure of the giant nucleic acid molecule known technically as deoxyribonucleic acid, or

DNA for short. DNA is believed to be responsible for the hereditary characteristics of cells; that is, it is the ultimate determiner of cell structure. DNA dictates the carbon copy reproduction of the cell and may be thought of as the information center of the cell.

Professors Crick and Watson unraveled the tangled architecture of the complex DNA molecule, and in the process, they discovered how DNA reproduces itself. They found that the DNA molecule has an intricate and most elegant geometrical design similar to that of a very long helical coil (or spiral staircase). The important aspect of its structure is that the DNA consists of a double chain, i.e., it has a paired structure. Along the length of the chains or strands there is a constant repetition of smaller chemical subunits known as nucleotides. There are four different kinds of nucleotides in DNA: adenine, cytosine, guanine and thymine. Each of these is joined to the long chain by means of a sugar-phosphate molecular group. The assemblage of nucleotide subunits, or beads on the strand, of DNA may include thousands of the four different kinds of beads, all arranged in a varied sequence. This intricate sequence of alternating nucleotide beads is a kind of molecular code, containing the genetic characteristics which are passed on from one generation to the next.

The immense variety of linear combinations of the four different nucleotide beads on the lengthy strands make possible a vast range of hereditary characteristics. But we have not as yet explained the duplication mechanism by means of which these characteristics are passed from the mother to the daughter cell. The explanation, according to Crick and Watson, lies in the paired, or duplex, structure of DNA. The twisted-ladder or circular-staircase structure of the DNA molecule contains rungs or connections each of which consists of a pair of nucleotides. The latter have a complementary relationship in that adenine and thymine bond together exclusively as do cytosine and guanine. The complementary arrangement of these nucleotides binds the two strands together. This neat pairing endows the

DNA molecule with a second, or duplex, strand whose properties are uniquely determined by the arrangement of nucleotides in the first strand.

When the cell divides, the DNA strands separate from each other and immediately the single strands attract nucleotides in the cellular environment. The four types of nucleotide beads fall into the prescribed places along the length of the DNA strand to form a complete second strand. By this simple but ingenious mechanism, the DNA molecule duplicates itself in every detail. The nucleotides are the building blocks which pair up to form DNA and then unzip to form identical DNA molecules. Several hundred million nucleotides may reside in the nucleus of a single cell and carry in encoded form the complete instructions for the development of the individual.

We have said that the DNA molecule reproduces itself with perfect order, but once in a great while errors or deviations in reproduction occur. These mistakes in reproduction are known as mutations. They are of fundamental importance because they introduce the element of variation and innovation into the evolutionary pattern. Genetic mutation is generally detrimental to the welfare of the cell or individual since only a very few mutations are classed as beneficial to the species. Most mutations upset the orderly development of the cell and may be lethal. This is the price which must be paid for genetic improvements. Of course, the goodness or badness of the mutation must be related to environment. A change produced by a mutation might be valuable to the survival of the individual on one planet but not on another. Thus while the mutation process may seem to be inefficient and wasteful, it must be viewed as a universal mechanism for allowing and furthering survival under a great variety of conditions.

Mutation conferred upon the giant molecule the ability to change, to experiment unknowingly with itself and to progress to a more complex assembly of molecules. It would be only natural for such increasing complexity to result in protection and containment of the molecular system, as within a cellular barrier or wall, and in specialization of function within the cellular entity. Step by step single cells evolved, perhaps as little colonies of similar cells, to multicellular existence. The record here is missing since it is long since buried and destroyed. The earliest fossil record goes back to the Cambrian Period of the Paleozoic Era, to roughly half a billion years ago.

The fossil record permits us to read back through the evolutionary book to the Ordovician Period, about 400 million years ago, when the first vertebrates, jawless fishes, appeared. From that time to the present the fossil record shows elaborate diversification of plants and animals, with mammals becoming dominant some 70 million years ago. Mammals existed long before then but apparently they did not evolve physiological features (fossil bones do not throw light on physiology) which equipped them for superior survival. Some creatures, like the common horseshoe crab seen on East Coast beaches, have undergone little evolutionary change in 200 million years. Others like man, a very recent innovation, exhibit speedy evolution, as is clear from the fact that we are distinctly unlike our predecessors of a million years past.

As one ponders the coming of man to this planet, it is inevitable that we should project our thoughts to other planets, not only in our own family but also on those orbiting distant stars. How common is "life"? Is man a unique creature of planet earth? These two questions need to be answered and guessed at separately, for it is one thing to talk of "life" and quite another to speak of man.

The layman finds little difficulty in drawing a line between a living and a dead organism. The scientist has more trouble because in the world revealed by the microscope there seem to be organisms on the borderline of life. Certain tiny viruses seem to be dead, but injected into a human being they quickly multiply, thus exhibiting one characteristic of life.

But there is no real need to pursue this point here because the kind of life of most concern to the layman is "intelligent life," and here we have criteria such as growth, reproduction, metabolism, mobility, reaction and adaptation which allow for unambiguous perception of life.

The answer to the first question about the commonness of life, meaning nonintelligent or rudimentary life forms, follows from our conclusion, assuming one grants its validity, that among the many billions of planets life should be rather common. The physical conditions of temperature limit the number of planets which qualify as hosts for life forms, but the total number of planets appears to be so astronomically large that even if only one planet in a thousand qualified, the remainder would be still numbered in the billions. It is futile to attempt an estimate of how many planets might have an environment resembling that of earth. However, life has evolved in a number of different environmental niches on earth and in a multitude of forms. On Mars the different atmosphere and soil will provide a nearby test ground for checking out our speculation about life on other planets.

In connection with the exploration of other planets, Dr. Joshua Lederberg raises the question of artificial panspermia— the transportation of earth-born organisms to extraterrestrial sites. He cautions:

> The introduction of microbial life to a previously barren planet, or to one occupied by a less well-adapted form of life, could result in the explosive growth of the implant, with consequences of geochemical scope. With a generation time of 30 minutes and easy dissemination by winds and currents, common bacteria could occupy a nutrient medium the size of the earth in a few days or weeks, being limited only by the exhaustion of available nutrients.

Dr. Lederberg has urged disinfecting all spacecraft in order to prevent planetary contamination or biomigration. He has also pointed to the possibility of back-contamination, that is, the transfer of extraterrestrial organisms to earth. "Since we are not yet quite certain of the existence of planetary (that is, Martian) organisms, and know nothing of their properties," he has said, "it is extremely difficult to assess the risk of the event.

The most dramatic hazard would be the introduction of new disease, imperiling human health." After arguing the pro and con of interplanetary infection, Dr. Lederberg concluded that a stringent embargo should be imposed upon the premature return of planetary samples.

Whatever the quest may yield, no one can dispute the grandeur of the chase in which the scientists are now engaged. From the molecule to the microbe and thence to man, from earth to the moon and to Mars—this is the broad arena of modern science. Man, the end product of an awesome evolutionary process, the only earth creature capable of conceptual thought, has learned how to alter his environment and to project his instruments, and eventually himself, beyond the bounds of his earth home.

He seeks to find if he is unique. He seeks to learn if somewhere in the universe a hospitable planet harbors intelligent life. His state of knowledge, and of technology, does not allow a definite answer and the frequently quoted statements of scientists must be classed as opinions. But the technology of space is augmenting our knowledge of the world around us. This accumulation of information and the powerful tools of modern science make for optimism about man's exploration of the unknown. But this hopefulness must be tempered with the fact that our planet occupies a most insignificant position in the scheme of the universe, and man, for all his ingenuity, faces certain natural and unalterable limits in his quest into space.

13

ACROSS THE VOID

ENRICO FERMI, the famous Italian scientist who contributed so much to our knowledge of the atom, once asked: "Where is everybody?" The question he posed was asked casually, but it carried profound implications. Fermi had, before his premature death, interested himself in problems about the origin of cosmic rays. This took him among the galaxies and to the heart of some universal problems. So when Fermi asked the seemingly commonplace question, he was thinking far beyond the framework of everyday life.

The question which Fermi asked transcended the mere existence of life elsewhere in the universe. In fact, Fermi asked it some years before the advent of the space age and the upswing of interest in extraterrestrial life. To my mind, Fermi assumed that life did exist beyond our solar system and the query he made reflected his puzzlement that "others" had not sought us out or in some way communicated with us. As between the

162

two possibilities—one, that a space vehicle could cross the great void and reach us, and, two, that a signal could be sent to us—the latter would be easier for a superior society. However, it presupposes that the society on the receiving end of the signal would be sufficiently advanced in its technology to respond to the communication.

Had any advanced society tried to communicate with our backward planet before 1960, it would have failed since no one was really equipped to "listen" for such a message. We will return to the problem of far-off communication after we consider the possibilities for direct, physical (meaning either space-probe or spaceship) exploration of deep space.

First, under the category of "deep space" we may consider the recesses of our own planetary system. Up to now we have discussed trips to Mars and Venus. We have made the point that in journeys within the solar system, our chemically powered space vehicles merely coast to their destination. The rockets just manage to overcome the earth's gravity field and to impart a slight velocity to the payload, which is then swept into a solar orbit by the long reach of the sun's gravity. Massive rockets of the Saturn type are required to propel a modest spacecraft to the nearby planets. Even more massive propulsion systems are required to hurl space vehicles to the edges of the solar system. To reach Neptune, for example, a launch velocity of ten miles per second has to be achieved. Such a spacecraft takes 31 years to complete a one-way mission to Neptune. Obviously such transit times are quite forbidding for manned voyages to the outermost planets. They are not even very attractive for space probes which cut the time in half by relaying the data back to earth at the velocity of light. Few experimenters are so patient that they will wait for half their adult lives in order to receive some data from a space probe.

More powerful rocket fuels of a chemical nature do not alter this situation very much. True, they may increase the final velocity of the space probe somewhat, but the transit times will still be discouragingly long. We have mentioned the nuclear rocket and Project Rover. The use of a nuclear power plant involves a concentrated fuel (one pound of uranium equals the heat output of a quarter million gallons of jet fuel) in a device known as a nuclear reactor. This machine "burns" nuclear fuel by splitting heavy atoms, and the energy released in the form of heat raises the core of the reactor to high temperature. The reactor is shown in Fig. 12 as a shielded cylinder

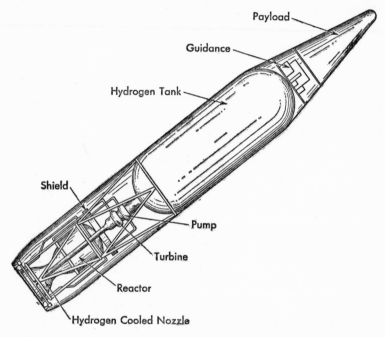

Fig. 12. Essential of a nuclear rocket. The heart of the nuclear power plant is the reactor core in which uranium fuel is "burned." *NASA*

mounted on top of a jet nozzle. Forward of the nuclear engine is a large tank of liquid hydrogen which is pumped through channels in the reactor core. The liquid hydrogen enters the reactor at minus 423° F. and is converted into a gas at high temperature (up to 4,000° F.). The expulsion of the hot exhaust gas through the rocket nozzle serves to propel the rocket forward, just as in the case of a chemically powered rocket.

Uranium fuel provides the heat which in the case of a chemical rocket comes from combustion of fuel and oxygen; the nuclear rocket has no requirement for oxygen since no combustion is involved.

Chemical fuels for modern rockets provide about 300 pounds of thrust for every pound of matter shot out the exhaust nozzle, and the best that one can hope for with chemical energy is about 400 pounds. The nuclear rocket is of superior thrust quality since it may provide from 800 to 1,200 pounds of thrust per pound of hydrogen used, depending upon the temperature achieved in the reactor core.

Project Rover is now a joint NASA-Atomic Energy Commission effort designed to perfect a nuclear engine for rocket applications. An experimental reactor, known as Kiwi-A, is designed to provide about 100,000 pounds of thrust. Thus it is not meant to be used as a booster engine but rather for upper stages of a vehicle like Saturn. If successful—a launchable nuclear stage is scheduled for 1965-66—the nuclear engine will improve the payload capability of Saturn. The nuclear stage can provide the advantage for low earth-orbital missions of high payload of reducing the number of stages required for the launch vehicle. For deeper space missions, nuclear rockets have the potential of increasing the payload five or six times over that of chemically powered rockets.

The difference between chemical and nuclear power can be illustrated for a manned, round-trip mission to Mars. Using chemical fuels, rocket experts would have to assemble a six-stage rocket with a thrust of 30 million pounds in order to project a 50-ton payload to Mars. If two nuclear stages are employed, the booster vehicle would require a thrust of four million pounds.

Krafft Ehricke, director of the Centaur program for Convair Astronautics, is enthusiastic about the prospects for nuclear propulsion in space. On March 24, 1960, he testified before a congressional committee: "Space will be conquered only by manned nuclear-powered vehicles. Planning anything else for the late sixties is, in my opinion, flirting with obsolescence almost from the start."

A much more ambitious nuclear project than Rover is the Orion rocket proposed by some atomic experts. The idea behind this project is that a big spaceship—one over a thousand tons —could be propelled in space by a series of "atomic pulses." These are really small nuclear explosions harnessed inside a reaction chamber so that each pulse accelerates the spaceship by two or three g's. The time scale for Project Orion is clearly well beyond that of Rover; indeed, its practicality remains to be demonstrated.

The propulsion systems we have described so far all employ high thrust. Systems with low thrust are being worked on. These are long-term developments which will probably pay off in the 1970's and 1980's. The idea behind low-thrust propulsion is that a space vehicle, once launched, can be accelerated by giving it a series of little pushes rather than one big push. Low-thrust systems would never get a rocket off the ground or slow it down quickly for re-entry, but they have the potential of powering space vehicles for a number of missions, such as shifting orbit or slow acceleration over long interplanetary journeys.

Low-thrust rocket systems include electrical-propulsion rockets, also known as ion or plasma rockets. Both types of rockets require large amounts of electrical power and it is presumed that on-board nuclear reactors would furnish this electricity. The advantage of the ion or plasma method of propulsion, as opposed to pumping liquid hydrogen through a nuclear reactor, is that there is the possibility of achieving higher exhaust velocities. For example, in the case of the ion engine the element cesium would be ionized, that is, stripped of an outer electron, and the beam of cesium ions would be boosted to high speed just as electrons are shot down the axis of a television tube. The exhaust ions could reach a velocity of hundreds of miles per second. Electrical propulsion systems are in about the same status today as jet engines were in the late thirties.

Additional and more advanced methods of space propulsion

are being considered but these show little hope of propelling any big space vehicle during the 1960's. Thus the outlook for the sixties and probably much of the seventies is for relatively low-velocity travel in space. This means that interplanetary travel will be based largely upon the energy which the earth shares with the space vehicle—orbital energy or, we might call it, original energy.

Present rocket fuels and even the nuclear-hydrogen engine limit spaceships to speeds of the order of ten miles per second and even engines now in the dream stage contemplate velocities "only" ten times higher. Even the latter, though highly impressive, keep man at a snail's pace in space as compared with the velocity of light. Yet it is the speed of light that becomes the velocity yardstick as we depart from the confines of the solar system and face the depths of space.

The star nearest to earth, apart from our sun, is Alpha Centauri. It lies 4.3 light-years distant or separated from us by 25,000,000,000,000 miles. Traveling at 100 miles per second, or three billion miles per year, it would take eight thousand years for an earth ship to reach Alpha Centauri. While it is the earth's nearest star, it is not likely to sponsor intelligent life. Alpha Centauri is a triple star system which is unfavorable to stable orbits for planets, and in addition, it is low on the stellar evolutionary scale. We must look deeper into space for an answer to Fermi's question.

Dr. Su-Shu Huang, Chinese-born astrophysicist now at the University of California, has conducted a systematic analysis of stars nearest to us, seeking to find those which might have planets suitable for supporting life. There are only half a dozen stars within ten light-years of our sun and none of these gives promise of possessing planets which would fulfill the condtions for life as set forth in the preceding chapter. Looking out to a distance of 15 light-years, i.e., scanning a spherical shell-zone 15 light-years in radius, Dr. Huang finds two candidates—Epsilon Eridani and Tau Ceti—which might have planets similar to Earth, Mars or Venus. These two stars, both less luminous and slower-burning than our sun, appear to be our best prospects as the home of some form of planetary life. This being the case, Dr. Su-Shu Huang observes: ". . . it may seem odd that we have had no visitors from other worlds." He goes on to provide an answer: "For one thing, the 10.8 light-years that separate us from Tau Ceti—astronomically a short distance—is an extremely long distance in terms of human experience."

"The abysm of time," as Shakespeare called it, looms as the great barrier to space voyagers. Is man an eternal prisoner of time or is it within his power to conquer its swift rush?

There are two answers to this question. In theory, the answer is in the affirmative, for Professor Einstein has given us his Special Theory of Relativity which relates time in systems that move with ultra-high velocity. In practice, the answer is obscure because of the difficulty of predicting what another century of rampant technology will bring. But it is a very long jump from ion rocket speeds of 100 miles per second to space vehicles which approach the velocity of light—186,000 miles per second. And it is only when one attains a speed close to that of light that the dimension of time alters markedly. The layman has certain convictions about time which boil down to the feeling that it is remorseless and unalterable. We have already described an orbital experiment involving an almost imperceptible alteration of time due to the weakening of the earth's gravitational field. In connection with the speeding up of time (a small effect) in the absence of gravity, we noted that the motion of the orbital device caused a slowdown in time. This latter effect is exceedingly small for vehicles moving at orbital velocity but it becomes increasingly important at velocities near that of light. Technically, it is know as time dilatation.

According to Einstein's special theory, the high-velocity space traveler does not age as rapidly as a stay-at-home. For example, if one of a pair of twins travels in a spaceship at close to the speed of light and makes a round-trip covering a hundred light-years, he would return to earth to find his twin long since dead, while he might have himself aged only twenty years. This asymmetrical aging, or clock paradox, has been disputed by some scientists, but a careful analysis by Nobel Prize winner Edwin M. McMillan led him to the conclusion that "the result, that travelers live longer than stay-at-homes, while sometimes called 'paradoxical' is really in the 'strange but true' category."

If the speedy twin never returned to earth but kept on in his space travels, he would not be aware of the contrast in time; to him the distances traveled would appear to be foreshortened. If the lay person has difficulty in grasping the meaning of the Einstein time effect, it is probably partly because the matter is so far removed from human experience. It may never be of practical value in space travel because of the inherent technical difficulty in propelling a space vehicle to higher and higher velocity. Photon rockets have been proposed for interstellar space travel; these would operate by using an exhaust of quanta of energy, or photons. A searchlight beam, for example, is a photon system but it is quite useless as a propulsive system. All attempts to achieve relativistic speeds are cursed by fantastic energy requirements since, as one gets close to the speed of light, prodigious energy is required for further acceleration. In fact, one needs to achieve total conversion of mass into energy to achieve relativistic space flight in contrast to the one-tenth-per cent conversion in uranium energy release. Even if speeds near the velocity of light appear only hypothetical, it adds to the intellectual excitement of the space era to consider them.

If we are restricted to the vicinity of the solar system in our space travels, there is little possibility for direct contact with planetary life beyond that of our own family. We are isolated in space, imprisoned by time. Fermi's question: "Where is everybody?" might be answered in a waggish manner: "Everyone's at home."

This still leaves us the communication channel. Again Professor Einstein enters the picture and imposes certain limits—specifically, a speed limit for space signals. It is fundamental to Einstein's theory that no signal can be transmitted with a velocity greater than that of light. This applies to all signals whether they be radio or light waves.

The Einstein signal limit is not of too much concern for communications on earth since the dimensions of our planet are small compared to the distance that radio waves travel in one second. Even over sun-earth distances there is only an eight-minute delay time in receipt of a solar signal. But as we go beyond the bounds of our solar system where distance is measured in light-years, then the Einstein limit becomes burdensome.

Suppose that we wish to carry on a conversation with "someone" on a planet orbiting Tau Ceti. It will take 10.8 years for the message to cross the void and an equal time for it to be returned, assuming, of course, that someone is at the end of the line who understands the message and is technically equipped to reply. A total pause of 21.6 years intervenes between query and reply. It would be quite improbable that, if life existed on this close-in planet, it would have reached a degree of technical sophistication that would enable it to carry on such long-distance communication. It might be a backward planet awaiting foreign aid.

Not finding a reply from Tau Ceti, we could transmit our signal beam deeper into space—out into a sphere swept by a radius of 50 or 100 light-years. This is only an infinitesimal cubicle in our Milky Way which is a fat discus-shaped galaxy some 100,000 light-years from edge to edge. Yet even inside this bit of space the travel times for light signals or radio waves are so great that whoever sends the message may not live to receive an answer. On the other hand we must take a long view of interstellar communications; our descendants may receive answers to the messages we transmit.

Even though we may not "talk" on the interstellar communication network, it will be a thrilling experience to pick up some signs of life from outer space—some faint, coded signals which indicate that we are not alone. Surely, if we have a spark of curiosity, we ought to be listening for such signals.

Scientists did not tune up delicate electronics ears for listening to our nearest space neighbors, who might be beaming messages at us, until 1960, when Project Ozma began. Ozma was the Queen of the mythical land of Oz which Frank Baum described as "a place very far away, difficult to reach and populated by strange, exotic beings." In a secluded area in the mountains of West Virginia, near the town of Greenbank, the U.S. National Radio Astronomy Observatory has been established. It is at this site, free from man-made interference, that giant electronic or radio ears will search the stars for signs of life.

Radioastronomy is a comparatively new science, especially in the United States, which is ironic because it was in this country that it was first discovered. The late Karl Jansky was working for the Bell Telephone Company in 1928, doing research on the very practical problem of looking for causes of static that interfered with the company's newly established radio-telephone service across the Atlantic. To search for possible origins of this static, he built a rotatable antenna on an abandoned farm near Holmdel, New Jersey, which first went into operation in the fall of 1930. It was tuned to receive electromagnetic (radio) signals having a frequency of about 21 megacycles, which is considerably higher than radio frequencies but somewhat lower than the channel frequencies allocated to commercial television. Karl Jansky picked up three kinds of disturbance or static. One he attributed to local thunderstorms, another to more remote atmospheric disturbances, and a third puzzled him. The signals seemed to come from space, probably from somewhere near the center of our Milky Way (26,000 light-years away). Karl Jansky had stumbled upon a discovery that was to become the science of radioastronomy and which would allow men to peer farther into space than they could with the largest optical telescopes. Yet for two decades almost nothing was done in this new field.

During World War II the development of radar focused upon electronic scanning of the sky for signs of approaching aircraft. Occasionally interference of extraterrestrial origin puzzled scientists working on radar development and, after the war, special radiotelescopes were built to track down the origin of these radio sources in space. As in the case of optical telescopes, the new device focuses the incident rays and because radio waves have such long wave length as compared to light waves, a vastly greater "mirror" is required. The reflector, or "dish," of the radiotelescope at Jodrell Bank, England, measures 250 feet from rim to rim, is steered by electric motors which orient it and its cradle so that it can be pointed almost anywhere in the sky. Such a device is a challenging construction assignment for engineers since the steel in the bowl and cradle weighs 800 tons. Built to scan the heavens for radio sources, the Jodrell Bank instrument became a vital link in space communications since it can be directed at space probes to receive faint radio signals across millions of miles.

The modern radiotelescope is capable of detecting radiosources in the remotest parts of the universe. Research has shown that a variety of celestial transmitters send their radio signals echoing throughout the stillness of space. The collision of galaxies, the excitation of hydrogen in stellar atmospheres, and a variety of causes produce radio signals. Judged by comparison with the power of radio stations on earth (usually several hundred kilowatts), these cosmic transmitters are incredibly powerful. A radio source in the constellation Cygnus, 270 million light-years distant, has been measured to have a transmitting power of a trillion billion billion times that of a powerful earth radio station.

The United States is building huge radiotelescopes in a somewhat belated effort to attain supremacy in a field it neglected for almost two decades. The first attempts to pick up radio signals from our closest neighbors where life might possibly exist, Tau Ceti and Epsilon Eridani, were made with the 85-foot radiotelescope, using a listening frequency of 1,420 megacycles. This particular communication channel appears to us as a favorable one since we know from receiving very distant radio signals that space is very transparent to it. In other words, it is a clear channel.

We have received no word from Tau Ceti or Epsilon Eridani. As Dr. Otto Struve, director of the National Radio Astronomy Observatory, concluded:

I believe that at the present time the probability of recording artificial radio signals from distances of the order of ten to twenty light-years is exceedingly small. But it is not zero, and the experiment must be performed. Only after there are more powerful radio-telescopes than those now available for this work will the volume of accessible space be sufficiently large to give us a choice of tens of thousands of stars that are likely to have planets in their habitable zones.

A 140-foot and a 300-foot radio telescope will extend man's listening range at the Greenbank facility, but these are dwarfed by even bigger developments. Plate 31 shows the "Big Dish," which is an $80-million radiotelescope designed by the U.S. Navy. The Navy has an interest in improving global communications and studying interference phenomena, so part of the "Big Dish" listening time will be reserved for military purposes. Located thirty miles due east of Greenbank, near the hamlet of Sugar Grove, where West Virginia notches its way into Virginia, the massive device is sited in a "quiet zone" 100 by 120 miles in area.

The "Big Dish" measures 600 feet in diameter and exposes seven acres of its metallic surface to catch radio waves from space. These are focused to a point indicated by the small cylinder nestled in the triangular web inside the three-legged support on the mirror surface. This cylinder constitutes the observation cage; it contains ultrasensitive electronic devices for amplifying and recording the radio signals. The huge structure soars to the height of a 66-story skyscraper. It can be rotated by trundling the entire structure on a double set of tracks at the base and by orienting it in its cradle; in this way it can be kept fixed upon a point in the celestial sphere despite the motion of the earth. Construction of rotatable structures of greater dimension is limited by cost and engineering problems. Larger fixed or nonsteerable dishes can be constructed but these participate in the earth's motion and thus sweep across the celestial sphere. Such a fixed reflector is located at Arecibo, Puerto Rico, where a 1,000-foot-diameter bowl of wire mesh is suspended a few feet above the surface of a natural sink-hole. Three huge towers support a cable system which keeps the wire-mesh surface spherical to within almost an inch. The 18-acre reflecting surface will be used for studying the radar characteristics of the nearby planets.

The Navy's 600-foot telescope will be used after 1964 for the transmission and reception of space messages. In other words, it will be capable of two-way conversation. But just how does one talk with "someone" else whom you have never met? Obviously, we must assume the existence of "intelligent life" and, in addition, an advanced technology. At our relatively primitive state of technology (in the first decade of space communication) any message we might dispatch into space might be regarded as baby talk. We could transmit very simple pulses so arranged in sequence that anyone receiving them would perceive that they were artificially ordered or coded. They would be simply recognition signals—opening wedges in more informative conversation with "them." But even this, if we are on the receiving end, would be epochal in human affairs. As Dr. Harold Urey put it: "Contact with *them* would be the most magnificent thing one can imagine."

Consider for a moment how primitive our earth technology may be in comparison with that of planet X. We have only just begun to build big radiotelescopes; we are only in the first decade of the space age. Our technological advancement is swift, to be sure, but measured on a time scale in which a thousand or a million years is just a tick, imagine the kind of technology that is possible in the future. What will our civilization be like in the year A.D. 2000 or A.D. 2,000,000?

The reason for asking this question is that our present society could well be at the A.D. 2,000,000 level of technology today. After all, the evolutionary process is keyed to statistical fluctuations, to random mutations. These could—on other planets or on this one—evolve biological systems at a rapid or a sluggish rate. I believe this is what Fermi had in mind when he asked, "Where is everybody?" He was, I believe, thinking of a society a million or ten million years more advanced than ours. Such a society would possess technological skills of which we have not the slightest inkling. Why, then, has such a society not got in touch with us?

We cannot be sure that space is silent, devoid of intelligently fashioned messages. We have only started to listen. And our means of projecting messages into space are very feeble, to say the least. I have heard some of my scientist friends say that silence in space might be explained very simply; they say that society cannot survive advanced technology, that the latter is self-destructive and, once the energy sources of matter are available, they become the final, lethal, evolutionary step. Perhaps so, and if so, what a grim commentary it is upon "intelligent" life.

Our failure to contact any neighbor in space will not prove that we are alone. Other interpretations are possible. We may not be seeking far enough in our galaxy (communication beyond the Milky Way is excluded). Or perhaps *they,* meaning an exo-society, have lost interest in contacting us—either because they have established other fruitful contacts (life may be common on a galactic scale) or they are bored waiting for life to make itself known in our solar system.

"A day will come," H. G. Wells wrote in 1901, "when beings who are now latent in our thoughts and hidden in our loins shall stand upon this earth as one stands upon a footstool, and shall laugh and reach out their hands amid the stars." When those who come after us reach out for the stars, they will be standing upon the foundation which we of the 20th century began to build so recently. They may smile, looking back at the pettiness of the U.S.-Soviet competition in space, but surely they will mark with respect the basic nobility of man's thrusting into space.

We peer into darkness. We feel for the pulse of other planets. We seek to know other worlds where life abides. An anonymous space-age poet has described the quest:

> How many worlds around their suns have woven
>   night and day,
> For countless thinking things like men, now deep
>   in stone, or clay!
> Their story, caught in light, now comes to us
>   unskilled to know
> The comedy, the tragedy, the glint of
>   friend or foe
> In that faint and cryptic message from afar,
>   and long ago.

GLOSSARY

AEC Atomic Energy Commission; U.S. agency charged with atomic development activity.

Aeros A NASA 24-hour weather satellite (1965).

Aphelion The orbital point at which a planet is farthest from the sun.

Apogee The orbital position when a planet makes its closest approach to the sun.

Apollo A spacecraft designed to carry a three-man crew on circumlunar flight (NASA, 1968).

Astronaut A space traveler. Name given to men manning the Mercury (NASA) orbital capsule.

Astronautics Science and technology of space flight.

Astrophysics Science of the physical aspects of luminous or stellar bodies.

Atlas A U.S. Air Force intercontinental ballistic missile used as a booster for space vehicles.

Atmosphere The gaseous envelope held to a planet by its gravity.

Big Joe Name given to the Atlas-Mercury rocket.

Booster Name given to the first stage of a multistage rocket.

Burn-out Cessation of combustion in the propulsion plant of a rocket.

Centaur Space vehicle which consists of an Atlas first stage and a Centaur, liquid hydrogen-powered, second stage.

Cosmic rays Penetrating radiation reaching the earth largely from outer space. A small fraction of the rays are emitted by our sun.

Courier A delayed-repeater, low-orbit communications satellite.

Discoverer A series of Air Force experimental satellites from which capsules are ejected for aircraft recovery.

Dish Term used to describe the metallic structure or wire mesh used as an antenna in space communications or in a radio-telescope.

Dyna-Soar A manned, military spacecraft rocket-boosted into orbit; designed for glide-re-entry.

Eccentricity The degree to which an orbit differs from circularity.

Echo A NASA passive, reflector satellite, inflated in orbit by pressure from sublimation powder.

Ecliptic Plane formed by the earth it its orbit about the sun.

EGO Eccentric geophysical orbiting satellite (NASA, 1961).

Escape velocity Speed required for a rocket to escape from a planet's gravitational attraction.

ESV Earth satellite vehicle.

Explorer Early U.S. experimental satellite.

Fission Splitting of the uranium atom with release of atomic energy.

Fusion Synthesis of light atoms such as hydrogen to form heavier atoms (helium) with release of atomic energy.

g Symbol for the Earth's surface gravity.

Ion An atom which has been stripped of an outer electron.

Jupiter U.S. Army ballistic missile used as a space booster.

Light-year Distance traveled by light in one year; numerically equal to 5.8 trillion miles.

Liquid fuel Any of a series of chemical compounds in liquid form which are used as a rocket fuel.

LOX Liquid oxygen.

Lunik Soviet space vehicles designed for lunar research.

Maria Named applied to the flat, dry seas on the moon.

Mariner Space probes in the 600-1,200-pound class design for interplanetary exploration (NASA, 1961).

Megacycle One million cycles per second.

Mercury Space capsule used for manned orbital flight (NASA).

Midas Air Force orbital device designed to provide early warning of missile attack.

NACA National Advisory Committee on Aeronautics, predecessor of NASA.

NASA National Aeronautics and Space Administration; the U.S. space agency.

Nimbus U.S. weather reconnaissance satellite (NASA, 1962).

Nova Engine generating 1.5 million pounds of thrust (NASA, 1968).

Orbit Trajectory of a space device about a parent planet or celestial body.

Orbital velocity Speed of a space vehicle or planet in its orbit.

Orion Project aimed at harnessing the power of small nuclear explosives to space propulsion.

Payload Useful weight of instruments or cargo projected on a space mission.

Perigee Point marking the closest approach of a satellite to the earth.

Perihelion Position of a planet or space probe at its closest approach to the sun.

Period Length of time required for one orbit.

Pioneer Early U.S. experimental satellite.

POGO Polar orbiting geophysical observatory in the 1,000-pound class (NASA, 1961).

Probe Unmanned, instrumented space vehicle projected beyond earth space.

Propellant Liquid or solid substances burned in rocket engines to provide thrust.

Prospector Lunar vehicle designed to be soft-landed (NASA, 1965).

Ranger Lunar vehicle designed for rough landings (NASA, 1962).

Radiation belt Also "Van Allen belt." A zone of charged particles surrounding a planet.

Redstone Short-range U.S. Army surface-to-surface missile.

Re-entry Process whereby a space vehicle returns to the earth's atmosphere.

Reactor Also nuclear reactor. Name given to a machine in which nuclear (uranium) energy is released at a controlled rate.

Retrorocket A rocket which is fired in a direction opposite to that of its motion.

Retrothrust Deceleration applied to a device by means of a retrorocket.

Samos Air Force, military, unmanned satellite for aerial reconnaissance.

Satellite As applied to man-made devices, a space vehicle in orbit about a planet—or moon.

Saturn Name given to both the booster and whole rocket of a U.S. high-thrust space vehicle. First stage, or booster, generates 1.5 million pounds of thrust (NASA, 1964).

Soft landing Deceleration of a space device by means of retrothrust so that the gadget makes gentle impact upon the moon or planet.

Solar cell Single unit of a solar battery which transforms sunlight into electrical energy.

Spectroscope Optical device used by astronomers to analyze composition and properties of stars.

Sputnik Literally "fellow traveler," it is the name given to the first Soviet earth satellites.

Surveyor Lunar space vehicle in 200-pound class designed for soft landing (NASA, 1963).

Telemetering Radio relaying of space data to receiving stations on earth.

Terrestrial Pertaining to the planet earth.

Thor Air Force intermediate-range ballistic missile, adapted for use as a space booster.

Thrust Propulsive effect produced by expulsion of hot gases from the exhaust nozzle of a rocket engine.

Tiros Early meteorological satellite (NASA).

Titan Air Force intercontinental ballistic missile.

Transit Navy navigational satellite.

Van Allen belt A radiation belt of ionized particles surrounding a planet.

Vanguard An early U.S. experimental satellite.

Voyager Space probe boosted by Saturn on interplanetary missions (NASA, 1965).

INDEX

Global television, 100-101
Goddard, Robert H., 48, 66
Goddard Space Flight Center, 48
Gravity, 3, 9-16, 21

Haldane, J. B. S., 153
H-bomb, 25
Hitler, 22
Huang, Su-Shu, 167-168

ICBM, 2, 19-20, 24-26, 34, 44, 118-119
International Geophysical Year, 28
Interplanetary flight, 123-126
Ion rocket, 166-168

Jaffe, Leonard, 133
Jansky, Karl, 171
Jet Propulsion Laboratory, 46, 76
Jodrell Bank, 136, 172
Johnson, Lyndon B., 4
Johnson, Roy, 24-25
Joliot-Curie, F., 75
Juno, 46
Jupiter C, 37, 84

Kepler, Johannes, 12, 14
Khrushchev, Nikita, 51, 73

Langley Field, 46
Lederberg, Joshua, 81, 151, 160-161
Lewis Laboratory, 46
Life, origin of, 146-161
Lipman, C. P., 153
Liquid fuel, 19, 23
Little Joe, 61
Lockheed Aircraft Corp., 76, 110, 114
Lomonosov, M., 75
Low, George M., 56
Lunik I (Mechta), 50
Lunik II, 51, 72-73
Lunik III, 72-75

Mariner (Project), 52
Mars, 8, 43, 52, 124-133, 142, 161, 163
Marshall Space Flight Center, 84, 87
McDonnell Aircraft Corp., 60
McElroy, Neil, 35

McMillan, Edwin M., 169
Medaris, John B., 35
Mercury, 8, 74, 123, 143
Mercury (Project), 52, 55-68
Meteors, 73
Micrometeorites, 49
Microminiaturization, 48
Midas (Project), 110-113
Milky Way, 140, 148, 170, 171, 175
Miller, Stanley L., 154-155
Missile mail, 20
Moffett Field, 46
Moon, 7, 13, 69-82
Moon trip, 3, 6, 53, 92-93
MOUSE satellite, 27
Mutation, 158

National Academy of Sciences, 27
National Advisory Committee on Aeronautics (NACA), 45, 60
National Aeronautics and Space Administration (NASA), 41, 45-54, 83, 91, 101, 105
National Radio Astronomy Observatory, 171, 173
National Science Foundation, 27
Neptune, 163
Nesmeyanov, A. D., 28
Newton, Isaac, 13-17
Nimbus (Project), 52, 98
North American Aviation Co., 84, 91
Notus (Project), 99-100
Nova (Project), 53, 79, 83, 91-94
Nuclear propulsion, 94, 163-167
Nuclear reactor, 164-166
Nucleic acid, 152
Nucleotides, 157-158

OAO, 105
Oparin, A. I., 153-154
Orbital bombing, 109, 117-119
Orbital flight, 6
Orbital refueling, 90
Orbiter, 78, 80, 130
Orion (Project), 166
Oxygen, 5, 80, 85
Ozma (Project), 171

ABOUT THE AUTHOR

Ralph E. Lapp is a scientist-writer whose books include *The New Force, Atoms and People, The Voyage of the Lucky Dragon* and *Roads to Discovery.* Besides technical articles and books, Dr. Lapp has written for the *Saturday Evening Post, Collier's, The Reader's Digest, Harper's* and *Life.*

Born in Buffalo, N.Y., Dr. Lapp completed his doctorate research in cosmic rays at the University of Chicago. He then devoted himself to nuclear resaerch on the A-bomb Project and at the end of the War he was appointed Assistant Director of the Argonne National Laboratory.

Dr. Lapp spent three years serving as scientific advisor to the War Department and as an atomic expert in the Defense Department. He has pioneered in discussing the impact of science upon society. A series of articles and lectures on radioactive fall-out and radiation hazards produced national and international repercussions.

A member of Phi Beta Kappa, Sigma Xi, the American Institute of Physics, the American Association for the Advancement of Science and the Philosophical Society of Washington, Dr. Lapp also takes an active interest in politics. He lives just south of Alexandria, Virginia with his wife and son. Dr. Lapp travels extensively and lectures throughout the United States.